THE
CARUS MATHEMATICAL MONOGRAPHS

Published by

THE MATHEMATICAL ASSOCIATION OF AMERICA

———

Publication Committee

THE CARUS MATHEMATICAL MONOGRAPHS are an expression of the desire of Mrs. Mary Hegeler Carus, and of her son, Dr. Edward H. Carus, to contribute to the dissemination of mathematical knowledge by making accessible at nominal cost a series of expository presentations of the best thoughts and keenest researches in pure and applied mathematics. The publication of the first four of these monographs was made possible by a notable gift to the Mathematical Association of America by Mrs. Carus as sole trustee of the Edward C. Hegeler Trust Fund. The sales from these have resulted in the Carus Monograph Fund, and the Mathematical Association has used this as a revolving book fund to publish the succeeding monographs.

The expositions of mathematical subjects which the monographs contain are set forth in a manner comprehensible not only to teachers and students specializing in mathematics, but also to scientific workers in other fields, and especially to the wide circle of thoughtful people who, having a moderate acquaintance with elementary mathematics, wish to extend their knowledge without prolonged and critical study of the mathematical journals and treatises. The scope of this series includes also historical and biographical monographs.

————

The Carus Mathematical Monographs

NUMBER SEVEN

VECTORS AND MATRICES

By

CYRUS COLTON MACDUFFEE

*Professor of Mathematics, Hunter College
of the City of New York*

Published by
THE MATHEMATICAL ASSOCIATION OF AMERICA

Composed, Printed and Bound by
The Collegiate Press
GEORGE BANTA PUBLISHING COMPANY
Menasha, Wisconsin

INTRODUCTION

The theory of matrices had its origin in the theory of determinants, and the latter had its origin in the theory of systems of equations. From Vandermonde and Laplace to Cayley, determinants were cultivated in a purely formal manner. The early algebraists never successfully explained what a determinant was, and indeed they were not interested in exact definitions.

It was Cayley who seems first to have noticed that "the idea of matrix precedes that of determinant." More explicitly, we can say that the relation of determinant to matrix is that of the absolute value of a complex number to the complex number itself, and it is no more possible to define determinant without the previous concept of matrix or its equivalent than it is to have the feline grin without the Cheshire cat.

In fact, the importance of the concept of determinant has been, and currently is, vastly over-estimated. Systems of equations can be solved as easily and neatly without determinants as with, as is illustrated in Chapter I of this Monograph. In fact, perhaps ninety per cent of matric theory can be developed without mentioning a determinant. The concept is necessary in some places, however, and is very useful in many others, so one should not push this point too far.

In the middle of the last century matrices were approached from several different points of view. The paper of Hamilton (1853) on "Linear and vector functions" is considered by Wedderburn to contain the beginnings of the theory. After developing some properties of "linear transformations" in earlier papers, Cayley finally wrote "A Memoir on the Theory of Matrices" in 1858 in which a matrix is considered as a single mathematical quantity. This paper gives Cayley considerable claim to the honor of introducing the modern concept of matrix, although the name is due to Sylvester (1850).

In 1867 there appeared the beautiful paper of Laguerre entitled "Sur le calcul des systèmes linéaires" in which matrices were treated almost in the modern manner. It attracted little attention at the time of its publication. Frobenius, in his fundamental paper "Ueber lineare Substitutionen und bilineare Formen" of 1878, approached matric theory through the composition of quadratic forms.

In fact, Hamilton, Cayley, Laguerre and Frobenius seem to have worked without the knowledge of each others' results. Frobenius, however, very soon became aware of these earlier papers and eventually adopted the term "matrix."

One of the central problems in matric theory is that of similarity. This problem was first solved for the complex field by means of the elementary divisor theory of Weierstrass and for other rings by H. J. S. Smith and Frobenius.

In the present century a number of writers have made direct attacks upon the problem of the rational reduction of a matrix by means of similarity transformations. S. Lattès in 1914 and G. Kowalewski in 1916 were among the pioneers, Kowalewski stating that his inspiration came from Sophus Lie. Since that time many versions of the rational reduction have been published by Dickson, Turnbull and Aitken, van der Waerden, Menge, Wedderburn, Ingraham, and Schreier and Sperner.

The history of these rational reductions has been

interesting and not without precedent in the field of mathematical research. The early reductions were short, requiring only a few pages. It is not prudent to say that any of the early papers is incorrect, for certainly a correct result was obtained in each case, but some of them contained arguments which were convincing only to their authors. The exposition in places was certainly too brief. Later writers subjected these difficult passages to closer scrutiny, as well as to the fierce fire of generalization, with the result that an adequate treatment was found to take many pages. The book of Schreier and Sperner, to which the present writer acknowledges indebtedness, contains 133 pages.

A large part of the profit which has come from this mathematical Odyssey has been the by-products. In attempting to justify certain steps in the proof, basic theorems on vectors and matrices were uncovered, theorems which had not previously come to notice. Of this origin are the theorems on the polynomial factors of the rank equation of a matrix—facts which should have been known long ago but which for some peculiar reason escaped discovery.

The present book is an attempt to set forth the new technique in matric theory which the writers on the rational reduction have developed. The long proofs have been broken down into simpler components, and these components have been proved as preliminary theorems in as great generality as appeared possible. With the background developed in the first five chapters, the rational reduction of Chapter VI does not seem difficult or unnatural.

That the vector technique will have other applications in matric theory than to the problem which brought it forth is quite certain. The Weyr theory for a general field was easily established (§55) once the key theorem (Corollary 57) was known. The orthogonal reduction (Chapter VIII) surrendered without a struggle.

The author wishes to express his appreciation of the kindness of Professors Richard Brauer, Marguerite Darkow, Mark Ingraham, and Saunders MacLane, who have read the manuscript and offered valuable suggestions. While no attempt has been made to credit ideas to their discoverers, it should not be out of place to state that the author has been greatly influenced by the work, much of it unpublished, of his former colleague, Mark Ingraham.

CYRUS COLTON MACDUFFEE

HUNTER COLLEGE OF THE CITY OF NEW YORK
September 1, 1942

TABLE OF CONTENTS

VECTORS AND MATRICES

CHAPTER I

SYSTEMS OF LINEAR EQUATIONS

1. Graphs. A *solution* of the equation

$$2x + 3y - 6 = 0$$

is a pair of numbers (x_1, y_1) such that

$$2x_1 + 3y_1 - 6 = 0.$$

There are infinitely many such solutions. A solution of the system of equations

(1)
$$2x + 3y - 6 = 0,$$
$$4x - 3y - 6 = 0$$

is a pair of numbers (x_1, y_1) which is a solution of both equations. There exists just one such solution, namely $(2, 2/3)$.

If we picture (x, y) as a point on the Cartesian plane, the infinitely many solutions of the equation

$$2x + 3y - 6 = 0$$

are the points of a straight line l_1, known as the *graph* of the equation. The second equation

$$4x - 3y - 6 = 0$$

also has a graph l_2 which is a straight line. The point of intersection of the two lines, namely $(2, 2/3)$, is the solution of the system of the two equations.

The point $(2, 2/3)$ is evidently the point of intersection of the line $x = 2$ with the line $y = 2/3$. Thus the problem of solving the system of equations (1) is equivalent

3

to the problem of finding the vertical line and the horizontal line which pass through the intersection point of their graphs.

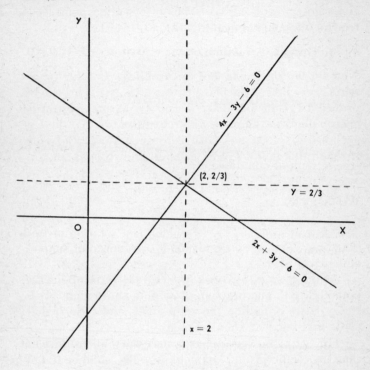

All methods of solving a system of equations such as (1) are but variations of one and the same process. Let k_1 and k_2 be any two numbers not both 0. The equation

$$k_1(2x + 3y - 6) + k_2(4x - 3y - 6) = 0,$$

or

$$(2)\quad (2k_1 + 4k_2)x + (3k_1 - 3k_2)y - 6k_1 - 6k_2 = 0,$$

is clearly the equation of a straight line, for the coefficients of x and y cannot both be 0 unless $k_1 = k_2 = 0$. This line passes through the intersection point of the two given lines; for if (x_1, y_1) is this intersection point, it is true for all values of k_1 and k_2 that

$$k_1(2x_1 + 3y_1 - 6) + k_2(4x_1 - 3y_1 - 6) = k_1 \cdot 0 + k_2 \cdot 0 = 0.$$

Now for various choices of k_1 and k_2, the line (2) represents every line of the plane through (x_1, y_1). This can be proved by showing that, if (x_2, y_2) is an arbitrarily chosen point of the plane different from (x_1, y_1), there is a choice of k_1, k_2 not both zero such that (2) passes through this point. Let k_1, k_2 be unknown, and set

$$k_1(2x_2 + 3y_2 - 6) + k_2(4x_2 - 3y_2 - 6) = 0.$$

We may choose

$$k_1 = 4x_2 - 3y_2 - 6, \qquad k_2 = -2x_2 - 3y_2 + 6.$$

Since (x_2, y_2) is not on both the given lines, not both k_1 and k_2 will be 0.

As the ratio $k_1 : k_2$ varies, the line (2) turns about the point (x_1, y_1). The problem of solving the system (1) is the problem of finding the values of k_1 and k_2 such that (2) is first vertical, then horizontal.

For (2) to be vertical, it is necessary and sufficient that the coefficient of y, namely $3k_1 - 3k_2$, shall be 0. Let $k_1 = k_2 = 1$. Then (2) becomes

$$6x + 0y - 12 = 0,$$

whence $x_1 = 2$. For (2) to be horizontal, it is necessary and sufficient that the coefficient of x, namely $2k_1 + 4k_2$, shall be 0. Let $k_1 = 2$, $k_2 = -1$. Then

$$0x + 9y - 6 = 0,$$

whence $y_1 = 2/3$.

2. Equivalence of systems. The principle illustrated in the above example is of general applicability, but when more than three unknowns are involved, or when the coefficient field is not real, the geometric interpretation becomes artificial. Suppose that we have a system of m equations in n unknowns,

(3)
$$f_1 = a_{11} x_1 + a_{12} x_2 + \cdots + a_{1n} x_n - c_1 = 0,$$
$$f_2 = a_{21} x_1 + a_{22} x_2 + \cdots + a_{2n} x_n - c_2 = 0,$$
$$\cdots\cdots\cdots\cdots\cdots\cdots\cdots\cdots\cdots\cdots\cdots\cdots$$
$$f_m = a_{m1} x_1 + a_{m2} x_2 + \cdots + a_{mn} x_n - c_m = 0,$$

with coefficients in any field. A *solution* of the equation $f_i = 0$ is a set of numbers $(x_1', x_2', \cdots, x_n')$ such that

$$a_{i1} x_1' + a_{i2} x_2' + \cdots + a_{in} x_n' - c_i = 0.$$

A solution of the system (3) is a set of numbers which is a solution of every equation of the system.

Suppose that there is another system of equations

(4)
$$g_1 = b_{11} x_1 + b_{12} x_2 + \cdots + b_{1n} x_n - d_1 = 0,$$
$$g_2 = b_{21} x_1 + b_{22} x_2 + \cdots + b_{2n} x_n - d_2 = 0,$$
$$\cdots\cdots\cdots\cdots\cdots\cdots\cdots\cdots\cdots\cdots\cdots\cdots$$
$$g_k = b_{k1} x_1 + b_{k2} x_2 + \cdots + b_{kn} x_n - d_k = 0.$$

The two systems (3) and (4) are called *equivalent* if every solution of each is a solution of the other.

The process of *solving* a system of equations is the process of finding an equivalent system of simplest possible form. Thus (3) is equivalent to

$$x_1 = h_{11} p_1 + h_{12} p_2 + \cdots + h_{1l} p_l + e_1,$$
$$x_2 = h_{21} p_1 + h_{22} p_2 + \cdots + h_{2l} p_l + e_2,$$
$$\cdots\cdots\cdots\cdots\cdots\cdots\cdots\cdots\cdots\cdots\cdots\cdots$$
$$x_n = h_{n1} p_1 + h_{n2} p_2 + \cdots + h_{nl} p_l + e_n$$

where $p_1, p_2, \cdots, p_l$ are parameters which may assume arbitrary values in the coefficient field.

Let us consider System (3). Let $k_1, k_2, \cdots, k_m$ be any numbers, and form the linear equation

$$k_1 f_1 + k_2 f_2 + \cdots + k_m f_m = 0.$$

Consider the system of equations

$$f_1 = 0,$$

$$\cdots \cdots \cdots \cdots \cdots \cdots$$

$$f_{i-1} = 0,$$

(5) $$\qquad k_1 f_1 + k_2 f_2 + \cdots + k_m f_m = 0,$$

$$f_{i+1} = 0,$$

$$\cdots \cdots \cdots \cdots \cdots \cdots$$

$$f_m = 0.$$

Clearly every solution of System (3) is a solution of System (5). Conversely, let $(x_1', x_2', \cdots, x_n')$ be any solution of (5). It is evidently a solution of every equation of (3) except possibly $f_i = 0$. But the i-th equation of (5) reduces to $k_i f_i = 0$, so if $k_i \neq 0$, it is also true that $f_i = 0$, and every solution of (5) is a solution of (3). Hence we have

THEOREM 1. *If in a system of equations* (3) *the i-th equation is replaced by*

$$k_1 f_1 + k_2 f_2 + \cdots + k_m f_m = 0, \qquad k_i \neq 0,$$

the new system is equivalent to the given system.

All methods of solving a system of equations, even the method by determinants, employ the above principle.

3. Elementary operations. There are three *elementary operations* which can be performed upon the equations of a system to yield an equivalent system. We shall call these the elementary operations of Types I, II and III. They are:

Type I. The interchange of two equations of the system.

Type II. The multiplication of an equation of the system by a number $k \neq 0$.

Type III.* The addition to any equation of the system of k times any other equation of the system.

The proof that each of these elementary operations when applied to a system of equations yields an equivalent system is now immediate. That an operation of Type I leaves the common solutions unchanged is evident. Operations of Types II and III are special cases of the operation of Theorem 1. Furthermore, the operation of Theorem 1 can be achieved by one operation of Type II followed by $m-1$ operations of Type III. That is, we first replace $f_i = 0$ by $k_i f_i = 0$ where $k_i \neq 0$, then replace this by $k_1 f_1 + k_i f_i = 0$, and so on.

4. Systems of homogeneous equations. Let us now restrict attention to a system of homogeneous equations

$$
\begin{aligned}
f_1 &= a_{11} x_1 + a_{12} x_2 + \cdots + a_{1n} x_n = 0, \\
f_2 &= a_{21} x_1 + a_{22} x_2 + \cdots + a_{2n} x_n = 0, \\
&\quad \cdots \cdots \cdots \cdots \cdots \cdots \cdots \cdots \cdots \\
f_m &= a_{m1} x_1 + a_{m2} x_2 + \cdots + a_{mn} x_n = 0.
\end{aligned}
$$

(6)

---

* These operations are not independent, for an operation of Type I can be obtained by a succession of operations of Type III with $k = 1$ and operations of Type II with $k = -1$.

A system of equations is called *triangular* if the last coefficient of f_{m-1} is 0, the last two coefficients of f_{m-2} are $0, \cdots$, the last $m-1$ coefficients of f_1 are 0. If $m > n$, this means that all the coefficients of $f_1, f_2, \cdots, f_{m-n}$ are 0 or, as we shall say, that these polynomials vanish.

THEOREM 2. *The system* (6) *of homogeneous equations is equivalent to a triangular system.*

If some coefficient of x_n is not 0, we can by an interchange of equations if necessary insure that $a_{mn} \neq 0$. By adding to the first equation $-a_{1n}/a_{mn}$ times the last equation, we can make the new coefficient in the place of a_{1n} equal to 0. Similarly we can make every coefficient of x_n except a_{mn} equal to 0. If at the start every coefficient of x_n was 0, no reduction was required.

Now ignore the last equation. Unless every coefficient of x_{n-1} (above $a_{m,\,n-1}$) is 0, we can assume that $a_{m-1,\,n-1} \neq 0$ and as before make every other coefficient of x_{n-1} equal to 0. In this way we obtain a system of equations of triangular form equivalent to (6). If $m > n$, the first $m-n$ equations have vanished, each coefficient having become 0, and possibly more than $m-n$ equations have vanished.

In every triangular system the number of non-vanishing equations is $m' \leq n$. By filling in with vanishing equations we may assume that $m' = n$. In this form the coefficients $a_{11}, a_{22}, \cdots, a_{nn}$ are called the *diagonal coefficients*. If the system is triangular, every coefficient to the right of the diagonal coefficients is 0.

THEOREM 3. *The system* (6) *of homogeneous equations is equivalent to one of triangular form in which every diagonal coefficient is either* 0 *or* 1; *and if the diagonal coefficient in any equation is* 0, *the equation vanishes.* Proof below

Let the equivalent triangular system be

$$
\begin{aligned}
a_{11}x_1 & & & = 0, \\
a_{21}x_1 + a_{22}x_2 & & & = 0, \\
a_{31}x_1 + a_{32}x_2 + a_{33}x_3 & & & = 0, \\
& \cdots \cdots \cdots \cdots \cdots \cdots \cdots & \\
a_{n1}x_1 + a_{n2}x_2 + \cdots + a_{nn}x_n & & & = 0.
\end{aligned}
$$

(7)

Suppose that the jth equation

$$
f_j = a_{j1}x_1 + a_{j2}x_2 + \cdots + a_{jj}x_j = 0
$$

is the last one which has its diagonal coefficient $a_{jj}=0$, but does not vanish. Let a_{ji} be the last coefficient of this equation which is not 0. If in the ith equation $a_{ii}=0$, we may interchange the ith and jth equations to obtain a new triangular system having one more non-zero diagonal coefficient and such that the new jth equation has one more zero coefficient to the right of its last non-zero coefficient. If, on the other hand, $a_{ii}\neq0$, we may add $-a_{ji}/a_{ii}$ times the ith equation to the jth equation and thus secure a new jth equation which either vanishes or has one more zero coefficient to the right of its last non-zero coefficient. In a finite number of steps we obtain a system in which every equation either vanishes or has a non-zero diagonal coefficient.

Now the non-zero coefficients of the diagonal can be made 1's by elementary operations of Type II.

THEOREM 4. *Every system of homogeneous equations is equivalent to a system of the form*

$$
\begin{aligned}
x_1 & = k_{11}p_1 + k_{12}p_2 + \cdots + k_{1,n-r}p_{n-r}, \\
x_2 & = k_{21}p_1 + k_{22}p_2 + \cdots + k_{2,n-r}p_{n-r}, \\
& \cdots \cdots \cdots \cdots \cdots \cdots \cdots \cdots \\
x_n & = k_{n1}p_1 + k_{n2}p_2 + \cdots + k_{n,n-r}p_{n-r}
\end{aligned}
$$

(8)

r defined on p. 11

where p_1, p_2, $\cdots$, p_{n-r} are parameters denoting arbitrary numbers of the coefficient field.

This form (8) is known as the *solved form* of the system of equations, or the *general solution* of (6). The process of reducing the system (6) to the system (8) is known as *solving* (6).

Let us start with a system of the form described in Theorem 3. A certain number, say $n-r$, of the coefficients in the sequence a_{11}, a_{22}, $\cdots$, a_{nn} will be 0. If a_{ii} is the first of these which is 0, give to x_i the arbitrary value p_1. If a_{jj} is the second which is 0, give to x_j the arbitrary value p_2, etc. Every other x is equal to a linear combination of x's with lower subscripts; so by eliminating these we reach the solved form of the system.

In particular, when $n = r$, (8) reduces to the system

$$x_1 = 0, \ x_2 = 0, \cdots, \ x_n = 0.$$

COROLLARY 4. *A system of $m < n$ homogeneous equations in n unknowns always has a solution not composed entirely of 0's.*

5. Systems of non-homogeneous equations. Let us denote by

$$f_1 = a_{11}\, x_1 + a_{12}\, x_2 + \cdots + a_{1n}\, x_n - c_1 = 0,$$
$$f_2 = a_{21}\, x_1 + a_{22}\, x_2 + \cdots + a_{2n}\, x_n - c_2 = 0,$$
(9)
$$\cdots \cdots \cdots \cdots \cdots \cdots \cdots \cdots \cdots$$
$$f_m = a_{m1}x_1 + a_{m2}x_2 + \cdots + a_{mn}x_n - c_m = 0$$

a system of m non-homogeneous equations in n unknowns. The equations (6), obtained from (9) by replacing each c by 0, will be called the *auxiliary homogeneous system*.

THEOREM 5. *If equations* (9) *have a solution, the general solution can be expressed as the sum of the general solution of the auxiliary system* (6) *and one particular solution of* (9).

We may write (9) in the abbreviated notation

$$\sum_{j=1}^{n} a_{ij}x_j = c_i \quad (i = 1, 2, \cdots, m).$$

Let $(x_1', x_2', \cdots, x_n')$ and $(x_1'', x_2'', \cdots, x_n'')$ be any two solutions of (9). Set $z_j = x_j' - x_j''$. Then

$$\sum a_{ij}z_j = \sum a_{ij}(x_j' - x_j'') = \sum a_{ij}x_j' - \sum a_{ij}x_j''$$

$$= c_i - c_i = 0,$$

so that $(z_1, z_2, \cdots, z_n)$ is a solution of (6). Then $x_j' = z_j + x_j''$. Now if $(x_1'', x_2'', \cdots, x_n'')$ is a particular solution of (9), we see that every solution is the sum of this particular solution and a solution of (6). Conversely every such sum is a solution of (9).

COROLLARY 5. *If n linear homogeneous equations in n unknowns have only the trivial solution composed entirely of* 0's, *then any non-homogeneous system having the given system as auxiliary system has one and only one solution.*

To solve a non-homogeneous system, we may proceed almost in the same manner as in the solution of a homogeneous system. A certain sequence of elementary operations will reduce the system (6) to the form of Theorem 3. This same sequence of elementary operations applied to the equations of the system (9) will reduce it to the form

That the non-homog. eq. has at least one sol. can be seen as follows: Since the homog. system of n eqs. in n unknowns has only the triv. sol., all its diag. elts. in triang. form, are 1. Hence no matter what the c's are, there is a sol. of the non-homog. eqs.

$$
\begin{aligned}
a_{11}x_1 & & - c_1 = 0, \\
a_{21}x_1 + a_{22}x_2 & & - c_2 = 0, \\
& \cdots \cdots \cdots \cdots \\
a_{n1}x_1 + a_{n2}x_2 + \cdots + a_{nn}x_n & - c_n = 0, \\
& & - c_{n+1} = 0, \\
& \cdots \cdots \cdots \cdots \\
& & - c_m = 0
\end{aligned}
$$

(10)

where either $a_{ii} \neq 0$ or else every a_{ij}=0. ~~every~~ a_{ij}=0 [$a_{ii}=0$ in which case]. The values of the a_{ij} and c_i in (10) are of course usually not the same as in (9).

If $a_{ii}=0$ in (10), or if $i>n$, the ith equation reduces to $c_i=0$, so if $c_i \neq 0$, the system (10) has no solution. If, on the other hand, $c_i=0$ whenever $a_{ii}=0$ or $i>n$, we may set $x_i=0$ for [for which $a_{ii}=0$] $i \leq n$ and solve the remaining equations step by step, thus obtaining a particular solution $(l_1, l_2, \cdots, l_n)$. We have proved

THEOREM 6. *A necessary and sufficient condition in order that the system of non-homogeneous equations in the diagonal form* (10) *have a solution is that every c_i shall be 0 if the corresponding coefficient a_{ii} is 0 or if $i>n$.*

COROLLARY 6. *A system of non-homogeneous equations* (9) *has a solution if and only if $k_1c_1+k_2c_2+ \cdots +k_mc_m=0$ for every set of numbers $k_1, k_2, \cdots, k_m$ such that*

$$k_1l_1 + k_2l_2 + \cdots + k_ml_m = 0,$$
$$l_i = a_{i1}x_1 + a_{i2}x_2 + \cdots + a_{in}x_n.$$

We shall state one more result, namely

Proof
If: suppose $k_1 c_1 + \cdots + k_m c_m = 0$ for every set of nos. $k_1, \cdots, k_m$ such that $\sum_{i=1}^{m} k_i l_i = 0$, $l_i = \sum_{n=1}^{n} a_{in} x_n$. Then (9) can surely be put in the form (10) with $c_i = 0$ if $a_{ii} = 0$ or $i > n$. By Thm. 6, then, (9) has a sol.
only if: suppose (9) has a sol. Then for this sol. $\sum_{n=1}^{n} a_{in} x_n = c_i$ $i = 1, \cdots, m$ and so if $\sum_{i=1}^{m} k_i l_i = 0$, Then $\sum_{i=1}^{m} k_i c_i = 0$.

THEOREM 7. *If the conditions of Theorem 6 are satisfied, (9) is equivalent to the system*

$$x_1 = k_{11}p_1 + k_{12}p_2 + \cdots + k_{1,n-r}p_{n-r} + l_1,$$
$$x_2 = k_{21}p_1 + k_{22}p_2 + \cdots + k_{2,n-r}p_{n-r} + l_2,$$
$$\cdot \quad \cdot \quad \cdot \quad \cdot \quad \cdot \quad \cdot \quad \cdot \quad \cdot \quad \cdot \quad \cdot \quad \cdot \quad \cdot \quad \cdot \quad \cdot \quad \cdot \quad \cdot$$
$$x_n = k_{n1}p_1 + k_{n2}p_2 + \cdots + k_{n,n-r}p_{n-r} + l_n$$

where $p_1, p_2, \cdots, p_{n-r}$ are parameters representing arbitrary numbers of the coefficient field, and $(l_1, l_2, \cdots, l_n)$ is a particular solution.

This theorem is a direct consequence of Theorem 5.

CHAPTER II

VECTOR SPACES

6. Vectors in ordinary space. We shall assume that the reader is familiar with the use of vectors in ordinary Euclidean space to represent physical quantities, such as forces, velocities, or accelerations, which have both magnitude and direction. Let there be a set of three coordinate axes not all in the same plane which we shall call the x-, y-, and z-axes. Let ϵ_1, ϵ_2, ϵ_3 be three line segments (basic vectors), each of length $\neq 0$, emanating from the origin, ϵ_1 on the x-axis, ϵ_2 on the y-axis, and ϵ_3 on the z-axis. Addition and scalar multiplication of line segments which lie on the same line are defined in the ordinary way.

Let ϕ be any line segment, or *vector*, emanating from the origin. A parallelepiped can be constructed having ϕ as a diagonal and having three of its edges on the respective coordinate axes. The edge which lies on the x-axis will be denoted by $a_1\epsilon_1$, the edge which lies on the y-axis by $a_2\epsilon_2$, and the edge on the z-axis by $a_3\epsilon_3$. Clearly a_1 will be positive if $a_1\epsilon_1$ extends in the same direction as ϵ_1, and a_1 will be negative if $a_1\epsilon_1$ extends in a direction opposite to that of ϵ_1. Relative to the basic vectors ϵ_1, ϵ_2, ϵ_3, the vector ϕ has the *components* or *coördinates* a_1, a_2, a_3, and we write

$$\phi = (a_1, a_2, a_3).$$

Conversely every triple (a_1, a_2, a_3) of three real numbers determines a unique vector ϕ. The *zero vector* $(0, 0, 0)$ is of length 0 so that its direction is quite immaterial.

The reader will recall that the *resultant* or *sum* of two vectors

$$\phi_1 = (a_1, a_2, a_3), \qquad \phi_2 = (b_1, b_2, b_3)$$

is the diagonal of the parallelepiped having the summands as adjacent sides, and that in terms of the co-ordinates of the vectors this is equivalent to the identity

$$\phi_1 + \phi_2 = (a_1 + b_1, a_2 + b_2, a_3 + b_3).$$

The reader will also recall that

$$k\phi = (ka_1, ka_2, ka_3)$$

is a vector lying on the same line as ϕ which is obtained by multiplying the segment ϕ by the number k. This vector $k\phi$ is called the *scalar product* of the vector ϕ by the scalar k. The vector $k\phi$ extends in the same or the opposite direction as ϕ according as k is positive or negative.

If ϕ_1 and ϕ_2 are two vectors which do not lie* in the same straight line, they determine a plane. Every vector in the plane (having, of course, one end at the origin) is of the form

$$k_1\phi_1 + k_2\phi_2,$$

and conversely every such vector is in the plane of ϕ_1 and ϕ_2.

Furthermore, if ϕ_1, ϕ_2, ϕ_3 are three vectors which do not lie in a plane, the set of all vectors

$$k_1\phi_1 + k_2\phi_2 + k_3\phi_3$$

* In deference to the usual notion that two vectors are equal if they have the same length and direction, we should word our assumption concerning ϕ_1 and ϕ_2 by saying that they are two vectors which cannot be laid on the same line. Similarly ϕ_1, ϕ_2, ϕ_3 are three vectors which cannot be laid on the same plane.

constitute all the vectors in space. We say that ϕ_1, ϕ_2, ϕ_3 *span* the vector space.

Three vectors span the space unless one of them lies in the plane containing the other two. That condition is equivalent to the statement that there exist three numbers k_1, k_2, k_3 not all zero such that

$$k_1\phi_1 + k_2\phi_2 + k_3\phi_3 = 0.$$

For if $k_1 \neq 0$, then ϕ_1 lies in a plane containing ϕ_2 and ϕ_3; and conversely. If $k_2 \neq 0$, then ϕ_2 lies in a plane containing ϕ_1 and ϕ_3, and so forth.

If ϵ_1, ϵ_2, ϵ_3 are mutually orthogonal unit vectors, the coördinates of ϕ are the cosines of the angles which ϕ makes with the respective ϵ's each multiplied by the length of the vector. If each of the vectors

$$\phi_1 = (a_1, a_2, a_3), \qquad \phi_2 = (b_1, b_2, b_3)$$

is of unit length, the cosine of the angle between them is

$$\cos \theta = a_1 b_1 + a_2 b_2 + a_3 b_3.$$

This expression is called the *inner product* or *scalar product* of the two vectors. If this inner product is 0, then $\cos \theta = 0$, and the vectors are *orthogonal*.

7. Vectors in general.* This geometric concept is easily generalized. We define an ordered set

$$\phi = (a_1, a_2, \cdots, a_n)$$

of n numbers of a field F to be a *vector* of *order* or *dimension* n, and call a_1, a_2, $\cdots$, a_n its components. Two such vectors are *equal* if and only if corresponding components are equal.

---

* A reader with a liking for the abstract may read Chapter IX at this point.

We define the operation of *scalar multiplication*, where k is in F, by the identity

$$k\phi = (ka_1, ka_2, \cdots, ka_n).$$

If $\phi_1 = (b_1, b_2, \cdots, b_n)$ is another vector, we define the *sum* by the formula

$$\phi + \phi_1 = (a_1 + b_1, a_2 + b_2, \cdots, a_n + b_n)$$

and the *inner product* by

$$\phi \cdot \phi_1 = a_1 b_1 + a_2 b_2 + \cdots + a_n b_n.$$

A set of vectors which is closed under the operations of scalar multiplication and addition is called a *linear system* of vectors, or a *vector space*. Thus if $\phi_1, \phi_2, \cdots, \phi_m$ are m vectors of order n, the set of all linear combinations

$$k_1 \phi_1 + k_2 \phi_2 + \cdots + k_m \phi_m$$

of these vectors, where $k_1, k_2, \cdots, k_m$ vary over F, is such a linear system S. The vectors $\phi_1, \phi_2, \cdots, \phi_m$ *span* S.

The same space may be spanned by many different sets of vectors, even by sets which contain different numbers of vectors. Thus the two vectors $(1, 0)$ and $(0, 1)$ span the same space that is spanned by the three vectors

$$(5, 2), \qquad (-1, 1/2), \qquad (1/3, 1).$$

Two sets of vectors which span the same space are called *linearly equivalent*.

The vectors $\phi_1, \phi_2, \cdots, \phi_m$ are *linearly dependent* (with respect to F) if m numbers $k_1, k_2, \cdots, k_m$ of F exist, not all zero, such that

$$k_1 \phi_1 + k_2 \phi_2 + \cdots + k_m \phi_m = 0.$$

If on the other hand every such relation implies that $k_1 = k_2 = \cdots = k_m = 0$, the vectors are *linearly independent*. We recall that in three-space three vectors are linearly dependent if and only if they are coplanar.

A set of vectors $\phi_1, \phi_2, \cdots, \phi_r$ which span S and are linearly independent constitute a *basis* for S.

THEOREM 8. *Every linear system of nth order vectors over F has a basis*

$$\phi_1, \phi_2, \cdots, \phi_r \qquad\qquad r \leqq n.$$

If there exist in S vectors all of whose components except the first are equal to 0, let

$$(a_{11}, 0, 0, \cdots, 0) \qquad\qquad a_{11} \neq 0$$

be one such vector, and call it ϕ_1. If there exist in S vectors of the form

$$(a_{21}, a_{22}, 0, \cdots, 0) \qquad\qquad a_{22} \neq 0,$$

choose one and call it ϕ_2, and so on. If there is a vector of the form

$$(a_{n1}, a_{n2}, \cdots, a_{nn}) \qquad\qquad a_{nn} \neq 0,$$

choose one and call it ϕ_n. Some of these types may not exist. Those which do exist give us a basis which, by a relabeling of the subscripts, we can call $\phi_1, \phi_2, \cdots, \phi_r$.

First we must show that these r vectors are linearly independent. It will be simpler notationally to assume a relation

$$k_1\phi_1 + k_2\phi_2 + \cdots + k_n\phi_n = 0$$

among the ϕ's as originally defined with the understanding that $k_i = 0$ if ϕ_i does not exist. Such a relation implies

$$k_1 a_{11} + k_2 a_{21} + \cdots + k_{n-1} a_{n-1,1} + k_n a_{n1} = 0,$$

$$k_2 a_{22} + \cdots + k_{n-1} a_{n-1,2} + k_n a_{n2} = 0,$$

$$\cdot \quad \cdot \quad \cdot \quad \cdot \quad \cdot \quad \cdot \quad \cdot \quad \cdot \quad \cdot \quad \cdot \quad \cdot \quad \cdot \quad \cdot \quad \cdot \quad \cdot$$

$$k_{n-1} a_{n-1,n-1} + k_n a_{n,n-1} = 0,$$

$$k_n a_{nn} = 0.$$

If ϕ_n exists, $a_{nn} \neq 0$, so $k_n = 0$. Thus $k_n = 0$ whether ϕ_n exists or not. Then, similarly, $k_{n-1} = 0$, and in fact every k_i is zero.

Finally we must show that every vector of S is a linear combination of these vectors. Let

$$\phi = (b_{n1}, b_{n2}, \cdots, b_{nn})$$

be any vector of S. If $b_{nn} \neq 0$, ϕ_n exists, and the vector

$$\phi - \frac{b_{nn}}{a_{nn}} \phi_n$$

exists in S, and has 0 for its last component. Let

$$\phi' = (b_{n-1,1}, b_{n-1,2}, \cdots, b_{n-1,n-1}, 0)$$

denote $\phi - b_{nn}\phi_n/a_{nn}$ or ϕ according as ϕ_n exists or does not exist. We proceed as before. If $b_{n-1,\,n-1} \neq 0$, then

$$\phi'' = \phi' - \frac{b_{n-1,n-1}}{a_{n-1,n-1}} \phi_{n-1}$$

has 0's for its last two components. Finally we have

$$\phi - \frac{b_{nn}}{a_{nn}} \phi_n - \cdots - \frac{b_{11}}{a_{11}} \phi_1 = 0,$$

$$\phi = \frac{b_{11}}{a_{11}} \phi_1 + \frac{b_{22}}{a_{22}} \phi_2 + \cdots + \frac{b_{nn}}{a_{nn}} \phi_n$$

where some of these terms will be missing if the corresponding ϕ_i do not exist.

COROLLARY 8. *Unless the linear system S contains a vector of the form* $(a_1, a_2, \cdots, a_i, 0, \cdots, 0)$ *with* $a_i \neq 0$, *for every* i, *then S has a basis of fewer than n vectors.*

We have now shown not only that every linear system S has a basis, but that there is a basis of a particularly simple form. Thus for $n = 3$ we have a basis

$$\phi_1 = (a_{11}, 0, 0) \qquad\qquad a_{11} \neq 0,$$

$$\phi_2 = (a_{21}, a_{22}, 0) \qquad\qquad a_{22} \neq 0,$$

$$\phi_3 = (a_{31}, a_{32}, a_{33}) \qquad\qquad a_{33} \neq 0$$

if all these ϕ's exist, but any one or any two of them might be missing. The extreme case where all three are missing is conceptually possible but trivial, since then S consists only of the 0-vector.

8. Rank of a linear system. The basis of a linear system is far from unique, but we shall prove the important theorem that the number r of vectors in a basis is the same for all bases. To this end we shall prove the simple but fundamental Replacement Theorem of Steinitz.

THEOREM 9. *Let* $\phi_1, \phi_2, \cdots, \phi_s$ *be linearly independent vectors, each linearly dependent upon the vectors* $\psi_1, \psi_2, \cdots \psi_r$. *Among* $\psi_1, \psi_2, \cdots, \psi_r$ *there exists a subset of s vectors which we may notationally take to be* $\psi_1, \psi_2, \cdots, \psi_s$ *such that* $\psi_1, \psi_2, \cdots, \psi_r$ *are linearly equivalent to* $\phi_1, \phi_2, \cdots, \phi_s, \psi_{s+1}, \cdots, \psi_r$. *Then* $s \leqq r$.

Let r be fixed $\geqq 1$ and let $s = 1$. The statement that "ϕ_1 is linearly independent" means that $k\phi_1 = 0$ implies $k = 0$—that is, that $\phi_1 \neq 0$. Then

$$\phi_1 = a_1\psi_1 + a_2\psi_2 + \cdots + a_r\psi_r$$

where not every a_i is zero. It is only necessary to relabel
the ψ's to insure that $a_1 \neq 0$. Then

$$\psi_1 = \frac{1}{a_1} \phi_1 - \frac{a_2}{a_1} \psi_2 - \cdots - \frac{a_r}{a_1} \psi_r.$$

Hence every linear combination of $\psi_1, \psi_2, \cdots, \psi_r$ is a
linear combination of $\phi_1, \psi_2, \cdots, \psi_r$, and the converse
is evident. Hence the theorem is true for $s = 1$.

The proof may be completed by induction. Suppose
the theorem to be true for $\phi_1, \phi_2, \cdots, \phi_{s-1}$. Then by the
induction hypothesis $\psi_1, \psi_2, \cdots, \psi_r$ are linearly equivalent to $\phi_1, \phi_2, \cdots, \phi_{s-1}, \psi_s, \cdots, \psi_r$, and in particular
ϕ_s can be written in the form

$$\phi_s = a_1\phi_1 + \cdots + a_{s-1}\phi_{s-1} + a_s\psi_s + \cdots + a_r\psi_r.$$

Not all of the $a_s, a_{s+1}, \cdots, a_r$ are 0, nor can it be true
that $r \leq s - 1$, for $\phi_1, \phi_2, \cdots, \phi_s$ are linearly independent.
It is a matter of notation to assume that $a_s \neq 0$. Then we
can write

$$\psi_s = b_1\phi_1 + \cdots + b_s\phi_s + b_{s+1}\psi_{s+1} + \cdots + b_r\psi_r.$$

Hence the sets $(\phi_1, \phi_2, \cdots, \phi_{s-1}, \psi_s, \cdots, \psi_r)$ and
$(\phi_1, \phi_2, \cdots, \phi_s, \psi_{s+1}, \cdots, \psi_r)$ are linearly equivalent.
The theorem is now proved.

COROLLARY 9a. *If $\psi_1, \psi_2, \cdots, \psi_r$ and $\phi_1, \phi_2, \cdots, \phi_s$
are two bases of the same linear system, then $r = s$.*

For in this case $\phi_1, \phi_2, \cdots, \phi_s$ are linearly independent, and each is equal to a linear combination of
$\psi_1, \psi_2, \cdots, \psi_r$. Hence $s \leq r$. Similarly $\psi_1, \psi_2, \cdots, \psi_r$ are
linearly independent and each is a linear combination of
$\phi_1, \phi_2, \cdots, \phi_s$ so that $r \leq s$. Hence $r = s$.

It is now proper to define the *rank* of a linear system
S of order n as the number of linearly independent vectors in a basis. By Theorem 8, S has a basis composed of

$r \leqq n$ linearly independent vectors, and by Corollary 9a this number r is the same for all bases. That is, the rank of S is the number of linearly independent vectors in any set of vectors which span S.

COROLLARY 9b. *If S is a linear system of rank n, then more than n vectors of S are always linearly dependent.*

COROLLARY 9c. *If S is a linear system of rank r, any r vectors of S form a basis for S if and only if they are linearly independent.*

COROLLARY 9d. *If $\phi_1, \phi_2, \cdots, \phi_s$ for $s < r$ are linearly independent vectors of S, it is possible to find $r - s$ vectors $\phi_{s+1}, \cdots, \phi_r$ such that $\phi_1, \phi_2, \cdots, \phi_r$ form a basis for S.*

9. The concept of matrix. A *matrix*

$$A = \begin{bmatrix} a_{11} & a_{12} \cdots a_{1n} \\ a_{21} & a_{22} \cdots a_{2n} \\ \cdot & \cdot \cdot \cdot \cdot \cdot \cdot \\ a_{m1} & a_{m2} \cdots a_{mn} \end{bmatrix} = (a_{rs})$$

may be thought of as an ordered set of vectors. That is, A consists of m rows, each row α_i being a vector. If A is an $m \times n$ array, it consists of m row vectors, each of order n. If $m = 1$, A is an ordinary vector of order n, so that the concept of matrix generalizes the concept of vector. Clearly A may be written

$$A = \begin{bmatrix} \alpha_1 \\ \alpha_2 \\ \cdots \\ \alpha_m \end{bmatrix} \qquad \alpha_i = (a_{i1}, a_{i2}, \cdots, a_{in}).$$

It is only natural to introduce two operations, *addition* and *scalar multiplication*, derived from the addition and scalar multiplication of vectors. Thus if

$$B = \begin{bmatrix} \beta_1 \\ \beta_2 \\ \cdots \\ \beta_m \end{bmatrix} \qquad \beta_i = (b_{i1}, b_{i2}, \cdots, b_{in}),$$

it is natural to define $A + B$ as follows:

$$A + B = \begin{bmatrix} \alpha_1 + \beta_1 \\ \alpha_2 + \beta_2 \\ \cdot \cdot \cdot \\ \alpha_m + \beta_m \end{bmatrix}$$

(11)

$$= \begin{bmatrix} a_{11} + b_{11} \cdots a_{1n} + b_{1n} \\ a_{21} + b_{21} \cdots a_{2n} + b_{2n} \\ \cdots \cdots \cdots \cdots \\ a_{m1} + b_{m1} \cdots a_{mn} + b_{mn} \end{bmatrix} = (a_{rs} + b_{rs});$$

and if k is any *scalar* (i.e., any element of the field F), we define the *scalar product* by means of the formula

$$kA = \begin{bmatrix} k\alpha_1 \\ k\alpha_2 \\ \cdots \\ k\alpha_m \end{bmatrix} = \begin{bmatrix} ka_{11} \cdots ka_{1n} \\ ka_{21} \cdots ka_{2n} \\ \cdots \cdots \\ ka_{m1} \cdots ka_{mn} \end{bmatrix} = (ka_{rs}).$$

If β is any vector, it is natural to define multiplication to be distributive. That is,

$$A\beta = \begin{bmatrix} \alpha_1 \\ \alpha_2 \\ \cdots \\ \alpha_m \end{bmatrix} \beta = \begin{bmatrix} \alpha_1\beta \\ \alpha_2\beta \\ \cdots \\ \alpha_m\beta \end{bmatrix}$$

which is a vector with components in F whose components are written in a column instead of in a row. Thus if

$$\beta = \begin{bmatrix} b_1 \\ b_2 \\ \cdots \\ b_n \end{bmatrix},$$

$$A\beta = \begin{bmatrix} a_{11} & a_{12} & \cdots & a_{1n} \\ a_{21} & a_{22} & \cdots & a_{2n} \\ \cdot & \cdot & \cdots & \cdot \\ a_{m1} & a_{m2} & \cdots & a_{mn} \end{bmatrix} \begin{bmatrix} b_1 \\ b_2 \\ \cdots \\ b_n \end{bmatrix}$$

$$= \begin{bmatrix} a_{11}\,b_1 + a_{12}\,b_2 + \cdots + a_{1n}\,b_n \\ a_{21}\,b_1 + a_{22}\,b_2 + \cdots + a_{2n}\,b_n \\ \cdot\ \cdot\ \cdot\ \cdot\ \cdot\ \cdot\ \cdot\ \cdot\ \cdot\ \cdot \\ a_{m1}b_1 + a_{m2}b_2 + \cdots + a_{mn}b_n \end{bmatrix}.$$

A matrix

$$B = \begin{bmatrix} b_{11} & b_{12} & \cdots & b_{1l} \\ b_{21} & b_{22} & \cdots & b_{2l} \\ \cdot & \cdot & \cdots & \cdot \\ b_{n1} & b_{n2} & \cdots & b_{nl} \end{bmatrix} = (b_{rs})$$

may alternatively be thought of as consisting of a row of l columns, each column being a vector

$$\beta_i = \begin{bmatrix} b_{1i} \\ b_{2i} \\ \cdots \\ b_{ni} \end{bmatrix}, \qquad B = (\beta_1, \beta_2, \cdots, \beta_l).$$

Then for any vector $\gamma = (c_1, c_2, \cdots, c_n)$ we define $\gamma \cdot B$ as follows:

$$\gamma \cdot B = \gamma \cdot (\beta_1, \beta_2, \cdots, \beta_l) = (\gamma\beta_1, \gamma\beta_2, \cdots, \gamma\beta_l)$$

$$= (c_1, c_2, \cdots, c_n) \begin{bmatrix} b_{11} & b_{12} & \cdots & b_{1l} \\ b_{21} & b_{22} & \cdots & b_{2l} \\ \cdot & \cdot & \cdots & \cdot \\ b_{n1} & b_{n2} & \cdots & b_{nl} \end{bmatrix}$$

$$= (c_1 b_{11} + c_2 b_{21} + \cdots + c_n b_{n1}, \cdots,$$

$$c_1 b_{1l} + c_2 b_{2l} + \cdots + c_n b_{nl}).$$

Now comes the problem of defining the product of two matrices. Clearly it would be possible to employ the definition $= (\beta_1, \beta_2, \cdots, \beta_l)$

$$AB = \begin{bmatrix} \alpha_1 \\ \alpha_2 \\ \cdots \\ \alpha_m \end{bmatrix} B = \begin{bmatrix} \alpha_1 B \\ \alpha_2 B \\ \cdots \\ \alpha_m B \end{bmatrix} = \begin{bmatrix} \alpha_1\beta_1 & \alpha_1\beta_2 & \cdots & \alpha_1\beta_l \\ \alpha_2\beta_1 & \alpha_2\beta_2 & \cdots & \alpha_2\beta_l \\ \cdot & \cdot & \cdots & \cdot \\ \alpha_m\beta_1 & \alpha_m\beta_2 & \cdots & \alpha_m\beta_l \end{bmatrix}.$$

But it would be an equally sensible definition if we wrote

$$AB = A(\beta_1, \beta_2, \cdots, \beta_l) = (A\beta_1, A\beta_2, \cdots, A\beta_l)$$

$$\begin{bmatrix} \alpha_1 \\ \alpha_2 \\ \cdots \\ \alpha_m \end{bmatrix} = \begin{bmatrix} \alpha_1\beta_1 & \alpha_1\beta_2 & \cdots & \alpha_1\beta_l \\ \alpha_2\beta_1 & \alpha_2\beta_2 & \cdots & \alpha_2\beta_l \\ \cdot & \cdot & \cdots & \cdot \\ \alpha_m\beta_1 & \alpha_m\beta_2 & \cdots & \alpha_m\beta_l \end{bmatrix}.$$

Fortunately both results are the same. We define, then, the product of two matrices A and B, the first composed of row vectors of order m, the second of column vectors of order m, to be the matrix whose element in row r and column s is the inner product of the rth row vector of A by the sth column vector of B. That is,

$$(12) \qquad AB = (a_{rs})(b_{rs}) = \left(\sum_{i=1}^{n} a_{ri}b_{is} \right).$$

Note that the product AB can be formed only when the number of columns of A is equal to the number of rows of B.

If B is an $m \times l$ matrix and O_m is an $m \times m$ matrix whose elements are all 0, then

$$O_m B = O$$

is an $m \times l$ matrix all of whose elements are 0. Similarly if O_l is an $l \times l$ matrix all of whose elements are 0, then

$$BO_l = O.$$

If B is square, $O_m = O_l = O$. Such matrices, all of whose elements are 0, are called *zero matrices*.

Let I_n denote the matrix

$$\begin{bmatrix} \epsilon_1 \\ \epsilon_2 \\ \cdots \\ \epsilon_n \end{bmatrix} = \begin{bmatrix} 1 & 0 \cdots 0 \\ 0 & 1 \cdots 0 \\ & \cdot \ \cdot \ \cdot \ \cdot \\ 0 & 0 \cdots 1 \end{bmatrix} = (\delta_{rs})$$

where $\epsilon_1, \epsilon_2, \cdots, \epsilon_n$ are the unit vectors of order n, and δ_{rs} is Kronecker's delta, denoting 1 for $r = s$ and 0 for $r \neq s$. If B is an $m \times l$ matrix, then

$$I_m B = (\sum \delta_{ri}b_{is}) = (b_{rs}) = B,$$
$$BI_l = (\sum b_{ri}\delta_{is}) = (b_{rs}) = B.$$

Thus I_n is called the *unit matrix* of order n. If B is square, $I_m = I_l$ is both a left and a right unit multiplier.

A matrix

$$\begin{bmatrix} k & 0 & \cdots & 0 \\ 0 & k & \cdots & 0 \\ & \cdot & \cdot & \cdot \\ 0 & 0 & \cdots & k \end{bmatrix} = (k\delta_{rs}) = kI$$

is called a *scalar matrix*. Since

$$kI + lI = (k + l)I, \qquad kI \cdot lI = (kl)I,$$

all the scalar matrices of a given order are isomorphic* under both addition and multiplication with the numbers of F.

The matrix $A^T = (a_{sr})$ is called the *transpose* of the matrix $A = (a_{rs})$, the second subscript denoting the row and the first subscript denoting the column in which an element stands. Thus a_{34}, which is in row 3 and column 4 of A is in row 4 and column 3 of A^T. The row vectors of A^T are the column vectors of A and vice versa. It follows directly from (11) and (12) that

$$(A + B)^T = A^T + B^T, \qquad (AB)^T = B^T A^T.$$

The first of these equations is obvious, and the second follows from the relation

$$(AB)^T = (\sum a_{si}b_{ir}) = (\sum b_{ir}a_{si}) = B^T A^T.$$

A correspondence such as $A \leftrightarrow A^T$ which reverses the order of multiplication but otherwise obeys the postu-

---

* A biunique correspondence

$$a \leftrightarrow a', \quad b \leftrightarrow b', \quad \cdots$$

between all the elements $a, b, \cdots$ of a set Σ and all the elements $a', b', \cdots$ of another set Σ_1 is an *isomorphism* relative to two corresponding operations $\circ$ of Σ and $\times$ of Σ_1 if

$$a \circ b \leftrightarrow a' \times b'$$

for all pairs of elements of the two sets.

lates for an automorphism is called an *anti-automorphism*.

self-isomorphism

Of fundamental importance is the fact that matric multiplication is associative. That is,

(13) $$(AB)C = A(BC).$$

This is immediately provable from (12), for each side of (13) is equal to

$$\left(\sum_{i,j} a_{ri} b_{ij} c_{js} \right).$$

Multiplication is not usually commutative, however. For instance,

$$\begin{bmatrix} 1 & 2 \\ 3 & 4 \end{bmatrix} \begin{bmatrix} 1 & 1 \\ 0 & 1 \end{bmatrix} = \begin{bmatrix} 1 & 3 \\ 3 & 7 \end{bmatrix},$$

$$\begin{bmatrix} 1 & 1 \\ 0 & 1 \end{bmatrix} \begin{bmatrix} 1 & 2 \\ 3 & 4 \end{bmatrix} = \begin{bmatrix} 4 & 6 \\ 3 & 4 \end{bmatrix}.$$

10. Rectangular arrays. One of the interesting and remarkable properties of matric multiplication is the following. Let C be a rectangular array of l rows and m columns, and let A be a rectangular array of m rows and n columns. Let

$$l = l_1 + l_2 + \cdots + l_p, \qquad m = m_1 + m_2 + \cdots + m_q,$$
$$n = n_1 + n_2 + \cdots + n_t$$

be any ordered partitions of l, m and n respectively. Draw lines through the arrays C and A separating them into arrays of subarrays C_{ij} and A_{ij}, respectively, such that C_{ij} has l_i rows and m_j columns, and A_{ij} has m_i rows and n_j columns.

Thus if

$$l = 6 = 3 + 3, \quad m = 4 = 2 + 1 + 1, \quad n = 4 = 2 + 2,$$

$$C = \begin{bmatrix} c_{11} & c_{12} & c_{13} & c_{14} \\ c_{21} & c_{22} & c_{23} & c_{24} \\ c_{31} & c_{32} & c_{33} & c_{34} \\ c_{41} & c_{42} & c_{43} & c_{44} \\ c_{51} & c_{52} & c_{53} & c_{54} \\ c_{61} & c_{62} & c_{63} & c_{64} \end{bmatrix} = \begin{bmatrix} C_{11} & C_{12} & C_{13} \\ C_{21} & C_{22} & C_{23} \end{bmatrix},$$

omit

$$A = \begin{bmatrix} a_{11} & a_{12} & a_{13} & a_{14} \\ a_{21} & a_{22} & a_{23} & a_{24} \\ a_{31} & a_{32} & a_{33} & a_{34} \\ a_{41} & a_{42} & a_{43} & a_{44} \end{bmatrix} = \begin{bmatrix} A_{11} & A_{12} \\ A_{21} & A_{22} \\ A_{31} & A_{32} \end{bmatrix}.$$

It is true that in general

$$CA = \left(\sum_{h=1}^{q} C_{rh} A_{hs} \right) \qquad (r = 1, \cdots, p; s = 1, \cdots, t).$$

That is, these subarrays behave in this situation like the elements of a matrix.

The idea of the proof can be obtained easily from the example without burdensome notation. The element in Row 4 and Column 2 of CA is

$$c_{41}a_{12} + c_{42}a_{22} + c_{43}a_{32} + c_{44}a_{42}.$$

This is the element in the upper right-hand corner of

$$C_{21}A_{11} + C_{22}A_{21} + C_{23}A_{31}.$$

In fact, the upper right-hand element of $C_{21}A_{11}$ contributes the first two terms, the upper right-hand element of $C_{22}A_{21}$ the next term, and the upper right-hand element of $C_{23}A_{31}$ the last term.

11. Elementary matrices. We define three types of *elementary operation* or *transformation* upon the rows of a matrix as follows:

Type I. The interchange of two row vectors.

Type II. The multiplication of the elements of any row vector by the same non-zero number of F.

Type III. The addition to any row vector of a multiple of any other row vector.

Thus the matrices

$$\begin{bmatrix} a_{21} & a_{22} & a_{23} \\ a_{11} & a_{12} & a_{13} \\ a_{31} & a_{32} & a_{33} \end{bmatrix}, \quad \begin{bmatrix} a_{11} & a_{12} & a_{13} \\ 3a_{21} & 3a_{22} & 3a_{23} \\ a_{31} & a_{32} & a_{33} \end{bmatrix},$$

$$\begin{bmatrix} a_{11} & a_{12} & a_{13} \\ a_{21} + 2a_{11} & a_{22} + 2a_{12} & a_{23} + 2a_{13} \\ a_{31} & a_{32} & a_{33} \end{bmatrix}$$

are obtained from $A = (a_{rs})$ by operations of Types I, II and III, respectively.

THEOREM 10. *The inverse of every elementary operation is an elementary operation of the same type.*

Clearly an elementary operation of Type I is its own inverse. The inverse of an elementary operation of Type II is obtained by replacing the multiplier by its reciprocal. The inverse of an elementary operation of Type III is obtained by replacing the multiplier by its negative.

THEOREM 11. *Every elementary operation upon the rows of a matrix leaves its row space invariant.*

The row space S of a matrix A is the space (or linear system) spanned by its row vectors $\phi_1, \phi_2, \cdots, \phi_n$. That the interchange of two of these vectors leaves S unchanged is trivial. Clearly every linear combination of either of the sets

$\phi_1, \phi_2, \cdots, c\phi_i, \cdots, \phi_n; \quad \phi_1, \phi_2, \cdots, \phi_i + k\phi_j, \cdots, \phi_n$

is a linear combination of $\phi_1, \phi_2, \cdots, \phi_n$, so S is not enlarged by a transformation of Types II or III. Since each transformation has an inverse of the same type, S is left unchanged by any transformation.

THEOREM 12. *Each elementary row operation is associative with matric multiplication.*

That is, if Ω denotes the row operation,

$$\Omega(AB) = (\Omega A)B.$$

Let $(a_{rs})(b_{rs}) = (\sum a_{ri}b_{is})$. We consider the three types of elementary transformation separately.

Type I: The first subscript of a is the row index in both A and in AB, so an interchange in the order of the rows of A brings about this same interchange in the order of the rows of AB, and produces no other change.

Type II: If the jth row of A is multiplied by c and the other rows remain unchanged, then the jth row of AB becomes

$$\sum_i ca_{ji}b_{is}.$$

That is, the jth row of AB will be multiplied by c.

Type III: Let the elements of the jth row of A be replaced by

$$a_{j1} + ka_{l1}, a_{j2} + ka_{l2}, \cdots, a_{jn} + ka_{ln},$$

the other rows remaining unchanged. Then the jth row of AB will be

$$\sum (a_{ji} + ka_{li})b_{i1}, \cdots, \sum (a_{ji} + ka_{li})b_{in}$$

which is equal to

$$\sum a_{ji}b_{i1} + k\sum a_{li}b_{i1}, \cdots, \sum a_{ji}b_{in} + k\sum a_{li}b_{in}$$

This is the same result that would have been obtained

from the application of the elementary operations to AB.

A matrix which is obtained from the identity matrix I by an elementary operation is called an *elementary matrix*. We have elementary matrices of each of the three types, exemplified respectively by

$$\begin{bmatrix} 1 & 0 & 0 & 0 \\ 0 & 0 & 0 & 1 \\ 0 & 0 & 1 & 0 \\ 0 & 1 & 0 & 0 \end{bmatrix}, \begin{bmatrix} 1 & 0 & 0 & 0 \\ 0 & c & 0 & 0 \\ 0 & 0 & 1 & 0 \\ 0 & 0 & 0 & 1 \end{bmatrix}, \begin{bmatrix} 1 & 0 & 0 & 0 \\ 0 & 1 & 0 & 0 \\ 0 & k & 1 & 0 \\ 0 & 0 & 0 & 1 \end{bmatrix}.$$

THEOREM 13. *Every elementary operation on the rows of a matrix can be accomplished by multiplying the matrix on the left by the corresponding elementary matrix.*

This follows directly from Theorem 12. For if Ω is any elementary row operation,

$$\Omega A = \Omega(IA) = (\Omega I)A.$$

The *row rank* of a matrix is the rank of the linear system spanned by its row vectors. That is, it is the number of its row vectors which are linearly independent.

THEOREM 14. *The row rank of a matrix is never raised by multiplying the matrix on the left by another matrix.*

Let

$$AB = \begin{bmatrix} a_{11} & a_{12} \cdots a_{1m} \\ a_{21} & a_{22} \cdots a_{2m} \\ \cdot & \cdot \cdot \cdot \cdot \cdot \cdot \\ a_{l1} & a_{l2} \cdots a_{lm} \end{bmatrix} \begin{bmatrix} \beta_1 \\ \beta_2 \\ \cdots \\ \beta_m \end{bmatrix} = \begin{bmatrix} \gamma_1 \\ \gamma_2 \\ \cdots \\ \gamma_l \end{bmatrix} = C.$$

Let $\phi_1, \phi_2, \cdots, \phi_s$ be a basis of the linear system defined by the γ's, and let $\psi_1, \psi_2, \cdots, \psi_r$ be a basis for the linear system defined by the β's. Since every ϕ_i is equal to a linear combination of the γ's, and every γ_i is equal to a linear combination of the β's, and every β_i is equal to a linear combination of the ψ's, it follows that $\phi_1, \phi_2, \cdots, \phi_s$ are linearly dependent upon $\psi_1, \psi_1, \cdots, \psi_r$. By Theorem 9, $s \leq r$.

A matrix is called *non-singular on the left* if there exists a matrix A^{-1} such that

$$A^{-1}A = I.$$

The matrix A^{-1} is called a *left inverse of A*.

THEOREM 15. *If A and B are each non-singular on the left, so is AB. A left inverse of AB is $B^{-1}A^{-1}$.*

For

$$(B^{-1}A^{-1})AB = B^{-1}(A^{-1}A)B = B^{-1}IB = B^{-1}B = I.$$

THEOREM 16. *Every elementary matrix is non-singular on the left, and has for an inverse the elementary matrix corresponding to the inverse row operation.*

From Theorem 10 we know that every elementary transformation Ω has an inverse so that, for the identity matrix I,

$$\Omega^{-1}\Omega I = I.$$

Let $\Omega I = E$, $\Omega^{-1}I = E^{-1}$. Then by Theorem 13, $E^{-1}E = I$.

THEOREM 17. *The row rank of a matrix is never changed by multiplying the matrix on the left by a matrix which is non-singular on the left.*

If B is of rank r, then AB is of rank $s \leq r$ by Theorem 14, and $A^{-1}AB = B$ is of rank $r \leq s$. Thus $r = s$.

COROLLARY 17. *The row rank of a matrix is never changed by an elementary transformation on its rows.*

12. A normal form. Every linear system of nth order
vectors can be spanned by n or less vectors (Theorem 8), and if
it is spanned by fewer than n vectors, we can adjoin
0-vectors to bring the number up to n. Hence every
space can be spanned by the row vectors of a square
matrix. In this section and in the sections immediately
following we shall assume that every matrix is square
with n rows and n columns.

The *principal* or *main diagonal* of a square matrix A
$= (a_{rs})$ is the sequence of elements $a_{11}, a_{22}, \cdots, a_{nn}$. The
matrix is *triangular* if every element above the principal
diagonal is 0.

THEOREM 18. *If A is a square matrix, there exists a
matrix P non-singular on the left which is the product of
elementary matrices such that PA is triangular with every
diagonal element either 0 or 1; if the diagonal element in
any row is 0, the entire row is 0; if the diagonal element in
any column is 1, every other element of the column is 0.
This form is unique.*

The first part of the proof is practically the same as
the proofs of Theorems 2 and 3. Let

$$A = \begin{bmatrix} a_{11} & a_{12} \cdots a_{1n} \\ a_{21} & a_{22} \cdots a_{2n} \\ \cdot \quad \cdot \quad \cdot \quad \cdot \quad \cdot \quad \cdot \\ a_{n1} & a_{n2} \cdots a_{nn} \end{bmatrix}.$$

Unless every element of the last column is 0, we can
interchange rows so that $a_{nn} \neq 0$. Add to the ith row
$-a_{in}/a_{nn}$ times the last row so that the new a_{in} will be
0. Thus in either case every element of the last column
above a_{nn} can be made 0. Similarly every element above
the principal diagonal can be made 0, so that a triangular matrix is obtained.

Let a_{ii} be the last diagonal element which is 0. Let a_{ij} be the last element of the ith row which is not 0. If $a_{jj}=0$, interchange the ith and jth rows. If $a_{jj}\neq 0$, add to the ith row $-a_{ij}/a_{jj}$ times the jth row. In either case the new element in the a_{ij} position has been made 0 without changing any element to the right of a_{ij} in the ith row or any element of a row below the ith. We continue until every element to the left of every 0 in the diagonal is 0.

By elementary transformations of Type II, every non-zero diagonal element can be made 1 without destroying the reductions which have been made. The following matrix is in the form thus far obtained:

$$\begin{bmatrix} 0 & 0 & 0 & 0 \\ a_{21} & 1 & 0 & 0 \\ 0 & 0 & 0 & 0 \\ a_{41} & a_{42} & a_{43} & 1 \end{bmatrix}.$$

Disregard the last row and let a_{ii} be the last diagonal element which is equal to 1. By adding $-a_{ni}$ times the ith row to the last row, we can make the new a_{ni} equal to 0. Similarly every element under a_{ii} which is not already 0 can be made equal to 0. Then if a_{jj} is the diagonal element equal to 1 which just precedes a_{ii}, every element under a_{jj} can be made 0. We proceed until the form described in the theorem is attained.

[margin note: not necessary since only place a non-zero elt. could be under this 1st one, is in the bottom row]

Each elementary operation was accomplished by multiplying the matrix on the left by an elementary matrix, and the product of these elementary matrices is the matrix P of the theorem. Since each elementary matrix is non-singular on the left, so is P, by Theorem 15.

This form of a matrix will be called the *Hermite*

canonical form, for it was first discovered by Hermite for non-singular matrices whose elements were rational integers.

Notice that the row vectors of the Hermite form constitute a basis for the row space of the type described in Theorem 8, and the rows which are not 0 are linearly independent. Thus the row rank of a matrix is equal to the number of non-zero rows in its Hermite canonical form.

We shall now prove that the Hermite form is unique. Consider the equation $PH=A$ where P is non-singular. We assume that H and A are in Hermite form, and shall show that $A=H$. It is true, then, that every h_{ii} is either 0 or 1; if $h_{ii}=0$, then every element of the ith row is 0; and if $h_{ii}=1$, then every other element of the ith column is 0. The same normalization holds for the elements of A.

The reader may be able to follow the proof more easily by keeping in mind the example

$$\begin{bmatrix} p_{11} & p_{12} & p_{13} & p_{14} \\ p_{21} & p_{22} & p_{23} & p_{24} \\ p_{31} & p_{32} & p_{33} & p_{34} \\ p_{41} & p_{42} & p_{43} & p_{44} \end{bmatrix} \begin{bmatrix} 0 & 0 & 0 & 0 \\ 2 & 1 & 0 & 0 \\ 0 & 0 & 0 & 0 \\ 3 & 0 & -1 & 1 \end{bmatrix}$$

$$= \begin{bmatrix} a_{11} & 0 & 0 & 0 \\ a_{21} & a_{22} & 0 & 0 \\ a_{31} & a_{32} & a_{33} & 0 \\ a_{41} & a_{42} & a_{43} & a_{44} \end{bmatrix}.$$

If the ith column of H has 1 in the main diagonal (and consequently 0's in every other position), then the ith column of P is equal to the ith column of A. The undetermined columns of P correspond to rows of 0's of H, so that the product of every ith row of P by the ith column of H is $p_{ii}h_{ii}$, and this must equal a_{ii}. If $h_{ii}=0$, then $a_{ii}=0$. Since H and A are of the same rank, $h_{ii}\neq 0$ implies $a_{ii}\neq 0$ and therefore $a_{ii}=1$. Then $a_{ji}=0$ for $j>i$, since A is in Hermite form, and every column of P which corresponds to a non-zero row of H is a column vector with 1 in the main diagonal and 0's elsewhere. Such a matrix P leaves H unaltered when used as a left multiplier so that $A=H$.

13. Non-singular matrices. Let us now take the special case of a square matrix A of order and rank n.

THEOREM 19. *If the rows of a square matrix are linearly independent, it is non-singular on the left, and conversely.*

Let $PA=H$ where H is the Hermite form. Since P is non-singular on the left, the row rank of A is equal to the row rank of H. If H had any zeros in its principal diagonal, the row rank of H would be less than n, contradicting the hypothesis that A is of row rank n. Hence $H=I$. Since $PA=I$, A is non-singular on the left.

If A is non-singular on the left, there exists a matrix P such that $PA=I$. The row rank of I is n so that, by Theorem 14, the row rank of A is n. This proves the converse.

THEOREM 20. *Every square matrix which is non-singular on the left is equal to a product of elementary matrices, and has a left inverse which is also equal to a product of elementary matrices.*

For if A is non-singular on the left, it is of rank n, its Hermite form is I, and there exists a matrix P which is a product of elementary matrices such that $PA=I$. Let

$$PA = E_k E_{k-1} \cdots E_2 E_1 A = I.$$

Then, upon multiplying on the left by the inverses, we have

$$A = E_1^{-1} E_2^{-1} \cdots E_{k-1}^{-1} E_k^{-1}.$$

But the inverse of an elementary matrix is an elementary matrix by Theorem 10. Thus A is a product of elementary matrices.

If a matrix A^* exists such that $AA^* = I$, then A is called *non-singular on the right*, and A^* is called a *right inverse* of A.

THEOREM 21. *If A is non-singular on the left, it is also non-singular on the right, and conversely.*

If A is non-singular on the left, there exists by Theorem 20 a matrix $\qquad$ *by converse and fact that $H = I$*

$$P = E_k E_{k-1} \cdots E_2 E_1$$

such that $PA = I$, the E's being elementary matrices. Then *multiplying $(E_k E_{k-1} \cdots E_2 E_1) A = I$ on the left by the left inverses*

$$A = E_1^{-1} E_2^{-1} \cdots E_{k-1}^{-1} E_k^{-1},$$

and

$$AP = E_1^{-1} E_2^{-1} \cdots E_{k-1}^{-1} E_k^{-1} E_k E_{k-1} \cdots E_2 E_1 = I.$$

The converse is similarly proved.

By virtue of this theorem, square matrices are either singular or non-singular, and we may drop the qualifying phrases "on the left" and "on the right."

THEOREM 22. *If A is non-singular, it has a unique left inverse and a unique right inverse, and these inverses are equal to each other.*

Suppose that A^{-1} is a left inverse and A^* a right inverse of A. Then

$$AA^* = I, \qquad A^{-1}A = I,$$
$$A^{-1}(AA^*) = (A^{-1}A)A^*$$

so that $A^{-1}I = IA^*$, whence $A^{-1} = A^*$. Thus every left inverse is equal to every right inverse.

We shall now speak of *the inverse* A^{-1} of a non-singular matrix.

14. Column vectors. A matrix A can equally well be considered as defining the linear system of its column vectors:

$$A = [\psi_1, \psi_2, \cdots, \psi_n], \qquad \psi_i = \begin{bmatrix} a_{1i} \\ a_{1i} \\ \cdots \\ a_{mi} \end{bmatrix}.$$

The reader will at once perceive the perfect duality of the two concepts. Every theorem of this chapter can be dualized by replacing "row" by "column" and making whatever changes are appropriate. The most important of these changes is that an elementary operation on the columns of a matrix is accomplished by multiplying the matrix on the right by an elementary matrix. (See Theorem 13.) The elementary matrices themselves are not different in form.

This duality can be at once established by replacing A by its transpose A^T. The column vectors of A become the row vectors of A^T. Then if

$$PA^T = H$$

where H is in the Hermite canonical form, it follows from (12) that

$$AP^T = H^T.$$

which leads directly to

$(PA^T)^T = (A^T)^T P^T = A P^T$

Thus H^T is the Hermite canonical form of a matrix under elementary transformations on its columns.

Two matrices A and B are called *equivalent* if two non-singular matrices P and Q exist such that

$$PAQ = B.$$

The term "equivalent" is justified by the following properties:

(a). A is equivalent to itself. For $IAI = A$.

(b). If A is equivalent to B, then B is equivalent to A. For $P^{-1}BQ^{-1} = A$.

(c). If A is equivalent to B and B is equivalent to C, then A is equivalent to C. For $PAQ = B$ and $RBS = C$ together imply $(RP)A(QS) = C$ with RP and QS non-singular. See Th. 15

THEOREM 23. *Every matrix A is equivalent to a diagonal matrix in which every diagonal element is either* 0 *or* 1.

By Theorem 18 we can find a matrix P such that $PA = H$ where H is in the Hermite form. In this form the only non-zero elements not in the principal diagonal are to the left of diagonal elements which are equal to 1. By elementary transformations on the columns, every non-diagonal element can be made 0. The following matrix in Hermite form will assist the reader in seeing this.

$$\begin{bmatrix} 1 & 0 & 0 & 0 & 0 \\ 0 & 0 & 0 & 0 & 0 \\ 0 & a_{32} & 1 & 0 & 0 \\ 0 & 0 & 0 & 0 & 0 \\ 0 & a_{52} & 0 & a_{54} & 1 \end{bmatrix}.$$

COROLLARY 23. *The row rank of a matrix is equal to its column rank.*

We note first that the theorem is true for the Hermite canonical form H. Those columns which have 1's in the principal diagonal are linearly independent, are r in number where r is the row rank, and every other column is a linear combination of these.

Now let A be any matrix. We may make it square by adjoining rows or columns of 0's without altering either its row rank or its column rank. Let $PAQ = D$ where PA is the Hermite form of A and D is a diagonal matrix having r diagonal elements equal to 1. Clearly both the row space and the column space of D are of rank r. The row rank of A is equal to the row rank of PA by Theorem 17, and we have just seen that this is equal to the column rank of PA. The column rank of PA is equal to the column rank of PAQ by the dual of Theorem 17. Thus the row rank of A is equal to r. Similarly the column rank of A is equal to the column rank r_1 of a diagonal matrix D_1 having r_1 diagonal elements equal to 1. Clearly D and D_1 are equivalent, and their row ranks are equal to their column ranks. If $P_1 D Q_1 = D_1$, the row rank of DQ_1 is r_1. But DQ_1 has at least $n-r$ rows of 0's so that $r_1 \leqq r$. Since $D = P_1^{-1} D_1 Q_1^{-1}$, $r \leqq r_1$.

We shall hereafter speak merely of *the rank* of a matrix.

We may, in fact, simplify the canonical form of Theorem 23 somewhat further by interchanging rows and columns so as to bring the 1's into the last r positions in the principal diagonal. Thus every matrix of rank r is equivalent to a matrix of the type

$$(14) \qquad \begin{bmatrix} 0 & 0 \\ 0 & I_r \end{bmatrix}$$

where I_r denotes the $r \times r$ identity matrix. This will be called the *canonical form of a matrix under equivalence transformations*.

15. Systems of equations. The system of equations

$$
\begin{aligned}
a_{11} x_1 + \cdots + a_{1n} x_n &= c_1, \\
a_{21} x_1 + \cdots + a_{2n} x_n &= c_2, \\
&\;\;\vdots \\
a_{m1} x_1 + \cdots + a_{mn} x_n &= c_m
\end{aligned}
$$

(15)

can be written in matric notation as

$$A\phi = \gamma$$

where

$$
A = \begin{bmatrix} a_{11} & a_{12} & \cdots & a_{1n} \\ a_{21} & a_{22} & \cdots & a_{2n} \\ \cdot & \cdot & \cdot & \cdot \\ a_{m1} & a_{m2} & \cdots & a_{mn} \end{bmatrix}, \quad
\phi = \begin{bmatrix} x_1 \\ x_2 \\ \cdots \\ x_n \end{bmatrix}, \quad
\gamma = \begin{bmatrix} c_1 \\ c_2 \\ \cdots \\ c_m \end{bmatrix}.
$$

THEOREM 24. *If A is an $m \times n$ matrix of rank r, there exist matrices P and Q where P is a product of elementary matrices and Q is a product of elementary matrices of Type I such that*

$$
(16) \quad PAQ = \begin{bmatrix}
1 & 0 & \cdots & 0 & k_{1,r+1} & \cdots & k_{1n} \\
0 & 1 & \cdots & 0 & k_{2,r+1} & \cdots & k_{2n} \\
\cdot & \cdot & & \cdot & \cdot & & \cdot \\
0 & 0 & \cdots & 1 & k_{r,r+1} & \cdots & k_{rn} \\
0 & 0 & \cdots & 0 & 0 & \cdots & 0 \\
\cdot & \cdot & & \cdot & \cdot & & \cdot \\
0 & 0 & \cdots & 0 & 0 & \cdots & 0
\end{bmatrix}.
$$

Let A be reduced to the Hermite form. There will be r 1's in the principal diagonal, any row containing a 0 in the principal diagonal will be a zero vector, and any column containing a 1 in the principal diagonal will be a unit vector. Now any permutation of the rows or columns will not change the number of these zero row vectors or the number of unit column vectors. By permuting the rows and columns, the 1's can be placed in the first r diagonal positions. The matrix will then be in the form (16). These permutations can be accomplished by multiplying the Hermite form on the right and left by elementary matrices of Type I.   *Q. E. D. Thm. 24*

By this means we again arrive at the solution of the system of equations (15). The matrix Q represents a certain permutation of the columns of A. Apply this permutation to the columns of A, and also to the unknowns $x_1, x_2, \cdots, x_n$, and relabel them in the normal order. Call the new matrix A'. Then there exists a matrix P such that PA' is of the form (16). To solve $A'\phi = \gamma$, we merely multiply on the left by P:

$$PA'\phi = P\gamma = \gamma'.$$

Now the vector $PA'\phi$ has its last $n - r$ components equal to 0, and its ith component is

$$x_i + \sum_{j=r+1}^{n} k_{ij}x_j \qquad (i = 1, 2, \cdots, r).$$

Hence unless the last $n - r$ components of γ' are 0, there is no solution. If these are 0, we have immediately the solution described in Theorem 7. (The x's from x_{r+1} on are arbitrary)

16. On the rank of a product. The following theorem which is readily provable at this point will be found useful later on.

[margin annotations:]
can use matrix at bottom p. 41 to illustrate the proof

At this pt. we can write (15) as, $A'\phi = \gamma'$. However we now relabel the x's and want to solve $A'\phi = \gamma$

which looks different from (15) since the unknowns are named differently, but is actually equivalent to (15)

(The corresponding row of the unknowns is moved)

since the naming of the unknown is irrelevant

since PA' has its last n-r rows equal to zero

THEOREM 25. *If A and B are $n \times n$ matrices of rank r whose row vectors span the same space, and if s is any integer $r \leqq s \leqq n$, there exists a matrix P of rank s such that $A = PB$.*

If A is of rank r, we can pass to the Hermite form and then permute rows so that

$$P_1 A = \begin{bmatrix} A_1 \\ O \end{bmatrix}$$

where A_1 is an $r \times n$ matrix whose row vectors α_1, $\alpha_2, \cdots, \alpha_r$, are linearly independent. Similarly we can write

$$Q_1 B = \begin{bmatrix} B_1 \\ O \end{bmatrix}$$

where $\beta_1, \beta_2, \cdots, \beta_r$ are the row vectors of B_1. Both P_1 and Q_1 are non-singular. If the rows of A and B span the same space, every row vector of A_1 is a linear combination of the row vectors of B_1, and vice versa. Thus there exist numbers $c_{ij}, d_{ij},$ of F such that

$$\alpha_i = \sum_{j=1}^{r} c_{ij}\beta_j, \qquad \beta_j = \sum_{k=1}^{r} d_{jk}\alpha_k, \qquad \alpha_i = \sum_{j,k=1}^{r} c_{ij}d_{jk}\alpha_k.$$

But $\alpha_1, \alpha_2, \cdots, \alpha_r$ are linearly independent, so

$$\sum_{j=1}^{r} c_{ij}d_{jk} = \delta_{ik}.$$

That is, $CD = I_r$, $A_1 = CB_1$, $B_1 = DA_1$ where

$$C = \begin{bmatrix} c_{11} & c_{12} \cdots c_{1r} \\ c_{21} & c_{22} \cdots c_{2r} \\ \cdot & \cdot \cdot \cdot \cdot \cdot \\ c_{r1} & c_{r2} \cdots c_{rr} \end{bmatrix}, \qquad D = \begin{bmatrix} d_{11} & d_{12} \cdots d_{1r} \\ d_{21} & d_{22} \cdots d_{2r} \\ \cdot & \cdot \cdot \cdot \cdot \cdot \\ d_{r1} & d_{r2} \cdots d_{rr} \end{bmatrix}.$$

Since C and D are inverses of each other, each is non-singular and hence of rank r. Now let

$$M = \begin{bmatrix} C & O \\ O & E \end{bmatrix}$$

where E is any $(n-r) \times (n-r)$ array. By §10,

$$MQ_1B = \begin{bmatrix} C & O \\ O & E \end{bmatrix} \begin{bmatrix} B_1 \\ O \end{bmatrix} = \begin{bmatrix} CB_1 \\ O \end{bmatrix} = \begin{bmatrix} A_1 \\ O \end{bmatrix} = P_1A.$$

Set $P = P_1^{-1}MQ_1$. Then $A = PB$. But E is arbitrary, so by a proper choice of E, M may be made to have any rank s from r to n inclusive. Since P_1 and Q_1 are non-singular, P has the same rank as M.

CHAPTER III

DETERMINANTS

17. Complex numbers. Consider the set of all matrices of the form

$$A = \begin{bmatrix} x & y \\ -y & x \end{bmatrix}, \qquad B = \begin{bmatrix} u & v \\ -v & u \end{bmatrix}, \cdots$$

where x, y, u, v, $\cdots$ are real numbers. The *sum* and *product*,

$$A + B = \begin{bmatrix} x+u & y+v \\ -(y+v) & x+u \end{bmatrix},$$

$$AB = BA = \begin{bmatrix} xu-yv & xv+yu \\ -(xv+yu) & xu-yv \end{bmatrix}$$

are both of the same form as A and B—that is, they have their diagonal elements equal to each other and the other two elements negatives of each other. In particular the zero matrix and the identity matrix,

$$O = \begin{bmatrix} 0 & 0 \\ 0 & 0 \end{bmatrix}, \qquad I = \begin{bmatrix} 1 & 0 \\ 0 & 1 \end{bmatrix},$$

are of this form. Thus the set of all matrices of this form is closed under addition and multiplication, and constitutes a *matric algebra with unit element*.

This algebra will be a field* if every matrix A except O has an inverse. The product AB will equal I if u and v are so chosen that

$$xu - yv = 1, \qquad yu + xv = 0.$$

* See §63 for the definition of a field.

47

The only possible solution is

$$u = \frac{x}{x^2 + y^2}, \qquad v = \frac{-y}{x^2 + y^2},$$

which exists for every A except $A = O$. Thus the above set of matrices is actually a field.

The correspondence

$$\begin{bmatrix} k & 0 \\ 0 & k \end{bmatrix} \leftrightarrow k$$

defines an isomorphism (§9) of a subset of our matric algebra with the real field R. The matrix A can be written

$$A = \begin{bmatrix} x & y \\ -y & x \end{bmatrix} = x \begin{bmatrix} 1 & 0 \\ 0 & 1 \end{bmatrix} + y \begin{bmatrix} 0 & 1 \\ -1 & 0 \end{bmatrix}$$

where

$$\begin{bmatrix} 1 & 0 \\ 0 & 1 \end{bmatrix} = I.$$

Clearly I corresponds to 1 under the above isomorphism. Moreover

$$\begin{bmatrix} 0 & 1 \\ -1 & 0 \end{bmatrix}^2 = \begin{bmatrix} -1 & 0 \\ 0 & -1 \end{bmatrix} \leftrightarrow -1.$$

Hence the correspondence

$$A = \begin{bmatrix} x & y \\ -y & x \end{bmatrix} \leftrightarrow x + yi$$

defines an isomorphism, or representation of the complex field as a matric algebra over the real field.

The polynomial $x^2 + y^2$ is the least common denominator of the elements of A^{-1} when x and y are indeterminates, and we denote this polynomial by $d(A)$ and call it the *determinant* of A. Every particular matrix A whose elements are real numbers has a determinant which is obtainable from $x^2 + y^2$ by giving to x and y their appropriate values.

If u and v also are indeterminates,

$$
\begin{aligned}
d(AB) &= (xu - yv)^2 + (xv + yu)^2 \\
&= x^2u^2 + y^2v^2 + x^2v^2 + y^2u^2 \\
&= (x^2 + y^2)(u^2 + v^2) = d(A) \cdot d(B).
\end{aligned}
$$

Thus the determinant of the product of the matrices which are isomorphic with two complex numbers is equal to the product of their determinants. If A corresponds to the complex number α, it is at once evident that $d(A)$ is the norm of α, that is, the square of its absolute value.

18. Matrices as hypercomplex numbers. Let F be any field, and let M consist of the set of all $n \times n$ matrices with elements in F. If

$$
A = (a_{rs}), \qquad B = (b_{rs}), \qquad C = (c_{rs}), \cdots
$$

are these matrices, we have defined (§9)

$$
A + B = (a_{rs} + b_{rs}), \qquad AB = \left(\sum a_{ri} b_{is} \right).
$$

It is clear that M is a commutative group* with respect to addition, the identity being the matrix O all of whose elements are 0. With respect to multiplication, however, we have only closure, the associative law, the distributive law, and the existence of the identity $I = (\delta_{rs})$. The two other properties which would be required for M to be a field are not necessarily present when $n > 1$, namely

---

* See §62 for the definition of group.

the commutative law of multiplication and the existence of the reciprocal of every matrix except O. Thus M is an instance of a *ring with unit element*.

We shall investigate the possibility of associating with every matrix of M a *valuation* or number $d(A)$ such that

$$d(AB) = d(A) \cdot d(B). \quad \circledast$$

Such a correspondence $A \rightarrow d(A)$ can always be accomplished by defining $d(A)$ to be 0 for every matrix A, or 1 for every matrix A, or 0 if A is singular and 1 if A is non-singular. But these valuations are quite trivial. If there is one non-trivial valuation where $d(A)$ is neither 0 nor 1 for some matrix A, there are infinitely many, for

$$A \rightarrow [d(A)]^k$$

is another non-trivial valuation for $k \neq 0, 1$.

(can be seen by raising both sides of ⊛ to the kth pwr.)

Let X and Y be two matrices whose elements are independent indeterminates x_{rs}, y_{rs}. We shall endeavor to find a polynomial $d(X)$ in the elements x_{rs} which is of lowest possible degree > 0 such that

(17) $$d(XY) = d(X) \cdot d(Y).$$

If such a polynomial can be found, then for every matrix A of M we may define $d(A)$ to be that number of F which is obtained by replacing the elements x_{rs} of X in $d(X)$ by the respective elements a_{rs} of A.

Since

$$d(X) = d(X \cdot I) = d(X) \cdot d(I)$$

from the fact that d(X) has degree it follows that d(X)≠0

and $d(X)$ is of degree > 0, it follows that $d(I) = 1$. Similarly

$$d(O) = d(X \cdot O) = d(X) \cdot d(O),$$

$$d(O) \cdot [1 - d(X)] = 0.$$

But $1 - d(X)$ is of degree > 0 *and hence not 0* so that $d(O) = 0$.

since d(X) is of degree > 0

We shall now attempt to determine the valuations of the elementary matrices. Nothing will be lost except complexity of notation if we restrict attention to the case $n = 3$.

Let

$$U = \begin{bmatrix} 0 & 1 & 0 \\ 1 & 0 & 0 \\ 0 & 0 & 1 \end{bmatrix}$$

be any elementary matrix of Type I. Clearly $U^2 = I$, so that

$$[d(U)]^2 = 1, \qquad d(U) = \pm 1.$$

Now let

$$V(k) = \begin{bmatrix} 1 & k & 0 \\ 0 & 1 & 0 \\ 0 & 0 & 1 \end{bmatrix}$$

be any elementary matrix of Type III, k being an indeterminate. Since $V(k) \cdot V(-k) = I$,

$$dV(k) \cdot dV(-k) = 1. \qquad \oplus$$

Now $dV(-k)$ is a polynomial in k of the same degree as that of $dV(k)$, and since the sum of their degrees is 0, each is a constant. Then $dV(k)$ has for every k the same value that it has for $k = 0$, namely 1.

since by $\oplus$ their product is 1

Let

$$W_1(l) = \begin{bmatrix} l & 0 & 0 \\ 0 & 1 & 0 \\ 0 & 0 & 1 \end{bmatrix}, \qquad W_2(l) = \begin{bmatrix} 1 & 0 & 0 \\ 0 & l & 0 \\ 0 & 0 & 1 \end{bmatrix},$$

be two elementary matrices of Type II which differ only

in the position of the indeterminate l in the main diagonal. Clearly

$$\begin{bmatrix} 0 & 1 & 0 \\ 1 & 0 & 0 \\ 0 & 0 & 1 \end{bmatrix} \begin{bmatrix} l & 0 & 0 \\ 0 & 1 & 0 \\ 0 & 0 & 1 \end{bmatrix} \begin{bmatrix} 0 & 1 & 0 \\ 1 & 0 & 0 \\ 0 & 0 & 1 \end{bmatrix} = \begin{bmatrix} 1 & 0 & 0 \\ 0 & l & 0 \\ 0 & 0 & 1 \end{bmatrix}$$

so that we have

$$d(U) \cdot dW_1(l) \cdot d(U) = dW_2(l).$$

Since $d(U) = \pm 1$, $dW_1(l) = d_2W(l)$. Hence we may denote $dW_i(l)$ by $dW(l)$.

It is easily seen that

$$\begin{bmatrix} l & 0 & 0 \\ 0 & 1 & 0 \\ 0 & 0 & 1 \end{bmatrix} \begin{bmatrix} 1 & 0 & 0 \\ 0 & l & 0 \\ 0 & 0 & 1 \end{bmatrix} \begin{bmatrix} 1 & 0 & 0 \\ 0 & 1 & 0 \\ 0 & 0 & l \end{bmatrix} = \begin{bmatrix} l & 0 & 0 \\ 0 & l & 0 \\ 0 & 0 & l \end{bmatrix} = S_l.$$

In the examples $n=3$

Hence the valuation of the scalar matrix S_l is the nth power of the valuation of $W(l)$. When $l = 0$ we have

$$(A) \qquad [dW(0)]^n = d(O) = 0,$$

so that $dW(0) = 0$.

Now $dW(l)$ cannot vanish for $l \neq 0$, for

$$W(l) \cdot W(1/l) = I,$$
$$dW(l) \cdot dW(1/l) = 1. \quad (B)$$

Thus $dW(l)$ vanishes when and only when $l = 0$, and hence has the form $c \cdot l^i$, where c is in F. But $dW(l) = 1$ when $l = 1$, so that $c = 1$.

We have shown that

$$d(U) = \pm 1, \quad dV(k) = 1, \quad dW(l) = l^i, \quad \boxed{i > 0,}$$
$$d[W(l) \cdot X] = dW(l) \cdot d(X) = l^i d(X).$$

by (A)

by (B)

(but an arbitrary one

Now $W(l) \cdot X$ is the matrix X with one of its rows multi-

since $W_i(l) = W_j(l)$ j arbitrary)

plied by l. Thus $d(X)$ is homogeneous of degree i in the elements of each row of X. For if it were not homog of deg. i in the

It is impossible to *prove* that $i = 1$ from (17) alone, for any power of $d(X)$ will satisfy (17) if $d(X)$ does. But we are seeking the valuation function of lowest degree, and it will yield the smallest consistent value of i in $dW(l)$ above. Our investigation from this point on will have to be tentative. We shall assume that $dW(l) = l$ and attempt under this assumption to find a $d(X)$ satisfying (17). If this proves to be impossible, we shall have to return to this point and assume a larger value for i.

We may now settle the ambiguity in the case of $d(U)$. From the equality

$$\begin{bmatrix} 1 & 0 & 0 \\ -1 & 1 & 0 \\ 0 & 0 & 1 \end{bmatrix} \begin{bmatrix} 1 & 1 & 0 \\ 0 & 1 & 0 \\ 0 & 0 & 1 \end{bmatrix} \begin{bmatrix} 1 & 0 & 0 \\ -1 & 1 & 0 \\ 0 & 0 & 1 \end{bmatrix} \begin{bmatrix} 0 & 1 & 0 \\ 1 & 0 & 0 \\ 0 & 0 & 1 \end{bmatrix}$$

$$= \begin{bmatrix} 1 & 0 & 0 \\ 0 & -1 & 0 \\ 0 & 0 & 1 \end{bmatrix}$$

it follows that

$$dV_3(-1) \cdot dV_2(1) \cdot dV_1(-1) \cdot d(U) = dW(-1).$$

Since $dV(k) = 1$ and $dW(l) = l$,

$$d(U) = -1.$$

We have now proved, subject to the assumption $dW(l) = l$ which will eventually be removed:

THEOREM 26. *Let U, V, $W(l)$ be elementary matrices of Types I, III and II, respectively. Then*

$$d(U) = -1, \qquad d(V) = 1, \qquad dW(l) = l.$$

The last equation also holds when $l = 0$.

19. Determinants. We have the result that

$$d[W(l) \cdot X] = dW(l) \cdot d(X) = l \cdot d(X).$$

Now $W(l) \cdot X$ is the matrix X with one of its rows multiplied by l. Thus $d(X)$ is homogeneous and linear in the elements of each row of X. Moreover,

$$d(UX) = d(U) \cdot d(X) = -d(X),$$

so that $d(X)$ merely changes sign when two rows are permuted.

Weierstrass defined a determinant as a polynomial in the elements x_{rs} of an $n \times n$ array X which is linear and homogeneous in the elements of each row, which merely changes sign when two rows are permuted, and which reduces to 1 when $X = I$. We have just proved that our function $d(X)$ has these properties so that we can identify the determinant of X with the valuation $d(X)$, and use the method of Weierstrass to obtain its explicit form.

Let us first consider the case where $n = 3$. Since $d(X)$ is linear and homogeneous in the elements of each row, it has the form

$$d(X) = \sum_{i,j,k=1}^{3} \epsilon_{ijk} x_{1i} x_{2j} x_{3k},$$

the ϵ_{ijk} being numbers of F. Let $X' = UX$ be obtained from X by the interchange of two rows, say the first two. Then

$$d(X) + d(X') = 0 = \sum (\epsilon_{ijk} + \epsilon_{jik}) x_{1i} x_{2j} x_{3k}.$$

Since the terms of this sum are linearly independent, it must be true that

$$\epsilon_{jik} = -\epsilon_{ijk}.$$

In general, if two coefficients are such that one is obtainable from the other by a single transposition of sub-scripts, they are negatives of each other. It then follows that ϵ_{ijk} is 0 unless the subscripts are distinct, provided F is not of characteristic 2; for if $i=j$, $\epsilon_{ijk} = -\epsilon_{jik}$ implies $2\epsilon_{ijk} = 0$.

When X reduces to I, $d(X)$ reduces to ϵ_{123}, which is therefore equal to 1. Hence ϵ_{ijk} is equal to 1 or -1 according as

$$\begin{pmatrix} 1 & 2 & 3 \\ i & j & k \end{pmatrix}$$

is an even or an odd permutation, and $d(X)$ is completely defined. It remains to be shown, however, that it meets our Requirement (17).

The same situation holds for any value of n. If X is an $n \times n$ matrix with indeterminate elements, we define

$$d(X) = \sum (-1)^h x_{1h_1} x_{2h_2} \cdots x_{nh_n}$$

where the summation extends over all permutations

$$\begin{pmatrix} 1 & 2 & \cdots & n \\ h_1 & h_2 & \cdots & h_n \end{pmatrix}$$

and h is a number of transpositions into which this permutation can be factored. Although h is not unique, it is shown in finite group theory that the oddness or evenness of h is unique.* Thus $d(X)$ is well defined.

If $A = (a_{rs})$ is an $n \times n$ matrix with elements in F, we define $d(A)$ to be the functional value of $d(X)$ under the substitution $x_{ij} \rightarrow a_{ij}$.

We shall now show that $d(X)$ meets our Requirement (17).

---

* See the author's *Introduction to Abstract Algebra*, Wiley and Sons, 1940, p. 72.

THEOREM 27. *If A and B are two matrices,*

$$d(AB) = d(A) \cdot d(B).$$

Consider a polynomial $f(X)$ in the elements x_{rs} of an $n \times n$ array X which is linear and homogeneous in the elements of each row, and which merely changes sign when two rows are permuted. We proceed just as in the derivation of the explicit form of $d(X)$ from the Weierstrass definition, except that we conclude that $\epsilon_{ijk} = \pm f(I)$. Thus $f(X) = d(X) \cdot f(I)$.

Let $X = (x_{rs})$ and $Y = (y_{rs})$ be two matrices whose elements are independent indeterminates, and form their product

$$XY = (\sum x_{ri} y_{is}).$$

Now $d(XY)$ is a linear homogeneous polynomial in the indeterminates x_{rs}. A permutation of the rows of X permutes the corresponding rows of XY; thus $d(XY)$ merely changes sign when two rows of X are permuted. Thus

$$d(XY) = d(X) \cdot K$$

where K is the value of $d(XY)$ for $X \rightarrow I$. Then

$$d(XY) = d(X) \cdot d(Y).$$

If A and B are two matrices with elements in F, we have

$$d(AB) = d(A) \cdot d(B).$$

20. The adjoint. As we have seen, $d(X)$ merely changes in sign when two rows of X are permuted. Therefore $d(A) = 0$ if A has two equal rows; for the permutation of these equal rows changes $d(A)$ into its negative, and yet obviously does not change $d(A)$ at all.

Hence*

$$d(A) = - d(A), \qquad 2d(A) = 0$$

and, if $2 \neq 0$, $d(A) = 0$.

We may write

$$d(X) = \sum_{h_i=1}^{n} x_{ih_i} \sum (-1)^h x_{1h_1} \cdots \; x_{i-1,h_{i-1}}, x_{i+1,h_{i+1}} \cdots \; x_{nh_n}$$

where the second summation extends over all permutations of the integers $1, 2, \cdots, n$ with h_i left out. This second summation depends upon both i and h_i, and we may denote it by X_{ih_i} and write

$$(18) \qquad d(X) = \sum_{j=1}^{n} x_{ij} X_{ij}.$$

We shall call X_{ij} the *cofactor* of x_{ij} in X.

It is important to note that X_{ij} is independent of the indeterminates $x_{i1}, x_{i2}, \cdots, x_{in}$ composing the ith row of X, and also of the indeterminates $x_{1j}, x_{2j}, \cdots, x_{nj}$ composing the jth column of X. Thus the n^2 cofactors X_{ij} have no common factor of degree > 0.

Let us replace in X the elements $x_{i1}, x_{i2}, \cdots, x_{in}$ of the ith row by the elements $x_{k1}, x_{k2}, \cdots, x_{kn}$ of the kth row, where $k \neq i$, and call the new matrix X'. Then X' will have two equal rows so that $d(X') = 0$. This substitution will have no effect upon the cofactors X_{i1}, $X_{i2}, \cdots, X_{in}$ of the elements of the ith row of X. Hence

$$d(X') = \sum_{j=1}^{n} x_{kj} X_{ij} = 0 \qquad\qquad k \neq i.$$

* If F is of characteristic 2 the argument has to be modified but the result is still true.

We can combine this equation with (18) to obtain

$$(19) \qquad \sum_{j=1}^{n} x_{kj} X_{ij} = \delta_{ki} \cdot d(X)$$

where δ_{ki} is Kronecker's delta.

The matrix

$$\text{adj } X = (X_{sr}),$$

where r denotes the row and s the column in which X_{sr} stands, is called the *adjoint* of X. The equation (19) above may now be written in matric notation as

$$X \cdot \text{adj } X = d(X) \cdot I.$$

Since $d(X)$ is not identically 0, we have

$$X \frac{\text{adj } X}{d(X)} = I.$$

That is, adj $X/d(X)$ is the inverse X^{-1} of X. Since $XX^{-1} = X^{-1}X$,

$$\text{adj } X \cdot X = d(X) \cdot I,$$

or

$$(20) \qquad \sum_{j=1}^{n} X_{jk} x_{ji} = \delta_{ki} \cdot d(X).$$

Relations (19) and (20) are of basic importance in determinant theory. We shall use them to prove two well-known theorems.

THEOREM 28. *Cramer's Rule. Let*

$$a_{i1}x_1 + a_{i2}x_2 + \cdots + a_{in}x_n = c_i, \quad (i = 1, 2, \cdots, n)$$

be a system of non-homogeneous equations whose matrix $A = (a_{rs})$ is non-singular. Let H_k be the matrix derived *from A by replacing its kth column by $c_1, c_2, \cdots, c_n$. The only solution of the system of equations is*

$$d(H_1)/d(A), d(H_2)/d(A), \cdots, d(H_n)/d(A).$$

If $(x_1', x_2', \cdots, x_n')$ is a solution of the given system, then

$$\sum_{j=1}^{n} a_{ij}x_j' = c_i.$$

Let A_{ik} be the cofactor of a_{ik} in the matrix A. Then

$$\sum_{i=1}^{n} A_{ik} \sum_{j=1}^{n} a_{ij}x_j' = \sum_{i=1}^{n} A_{ik}c_i,$$

$$\sum_{j=1}^{n} \left[\sum_{i=1}^{n} A_{ik}a_{ij} \right] x_j' = \sum_{i=1}^{n} A_{ik}c_i.$$

If in the sum $\sum A_{ik}c_i$ we replace c_i by a_{ik}, we obtain $d(A)$. Thus

$$\sum A_{ik}c_i = d(H_k)$$

is the determinant of the matrix H_k obtained from A by replacing the kth column by the c's. Making use of (20), we have

$$\sum_{j=1}^{n} \delta_{kj}d(A) \cdot x_j' = d(A) \cdot x_k' = d(H_k).$$

If $d(A) \neq 0$, our assumed solution can be nothing other than

$$(d(H_1)/d(A), d(H_2)/d(A), \cdots, d(H_n)/d(A)).$$

That this is actually a solution can be established by substituting it into the given equations.

It should be noted that this method of solving systems of equations is not fundamentally different from the method described in §1 and §2. The choice of the cofactors A_{ik} for the k's of Theorem 1 produces an equation all of whose coefficients vanish except the coefficient of x_k.

Another useful and familiar theorem is

THEOREM 29. *Let*

$$a_{i1}x_1 + a_{i2}x_2 + \cdots + a_{in}x_n = 0 \quad (i = 1, 2, \cdots, n)$$

be a system of homogeneous equations whose matrix $A = (a_{rs})$ *is singular. For every value of* k,

$$(A_{k1}, A_{k2}, \cdots, A_{kn})$$

is a solution.

From (19) we have

$$\sum_{j=1}^{n} a_{ij}A_{kj} = \delta_{ik}d(A) = 0,$$

which proves the theorem.

COROLLARY 29. *Let*

$$a_{i1}x_1 + a_{i2}x_2 + \cdots + a_{in}x_n = 0 \quad (i = 1, 2, \cdots, n - 1)$$

be a system of $n-1$ *homogeneous equations in* n *unknowns. Let* h_i *be* $(-1)^{i+1}$ *times the determinant of the matrix obtained by suppressing the ith column of* A. *Then*

$$(h_1, h_2, \cdots, h_n)$$

is a solution.

If we adjoin to the given system another equation all of whose coefficients are 0 and apply the theorem with $k = n$, we obtain the corollary. We shall see in §23 that the solution is trivial unless the rank of the matrix of the coefficients is $n - 1$.

21. Properties of determinants. The literature on determinants is vast and well known, and determinants are not the primary objective of this book. We shall therefore be content with the precise statement of a few of the principal results with an indication of their proofs.

In finding the determinants of the elementary matrices, we have proved three well-known theorems. Let U be the unit matrix I with its ith and jth rows interchanged. If A is any matrix, $B = UA$ differs from A only in having the ith and jth rows interchanged, and $B' = AU$ differs from A only in having the ith and jth columns interchanged. But $d(U) = -1$, so that

$$d(B) = -d(A), \qquad d(B') = -d(A).$$

Thus we have

THEOREM 30. *If the matrix B is obtained from A by the interchange of two rows or of two columns, $d(B) = -d(A)$.*

COROLLARY 30. *If two rows or two columns of A are identical, $d(A) = 0$.*

If F is of characteristic 2, a special proof is required, but the corollary holds for every field.

Let W be the elementary matrix obtained from I by replacing the 1 in the (i, i) position by l. Then WA is obtainable from A by multiplying each element of the ith row by l, and AW is obtainable from A by multiplying each element of the ith column by l. But $d(W) = l$, so we have:

THEOREM 31. *If B is obtained from A by multiplying each element of any row or any column of A by l, then $d(B) = l \cdot d(A)$.*

Let V_{ij} be the elementary matrix obtained from I by replacing the 0 in row i and column j by k. Then

$B = V_{ij}A$ is obtainable from A by adding to each element of the ith row k times the corresponding element of the jth row. But $d(V_{ij}) = 1$, so that B and A have the same determinant. Similarly $B' = A V_{ij}$ is obtainable from A by adding to each element of the jth column k times the corresponding element of the ith column, and similarly A and B' have the same determinant. By a repetition of the argument, we have:

THEOREM 32. *If B is obtained from A by adding to any row (or column) a linear combination of the other rows (or columns), then $d(B) = d(A)$.*

These results are also readily obtainable from the definition

$$d(X) = \sum (-1)^h x_{1i_1} x_{2i_2} \cdots x_{ni_n},$$

where h is a number of transpositions into which the substitution

$$s = \begin{pmatrix} 1 & 2 & \cdots & n \\ i_1 & i_2 & \cdots & i_n \end{pmatrix}$$

can be factored. In fact, all of the well-known determinant theorems come directly from this expression and the elementary theorems of finite group theory. Thus if X^T is the transpose of X,

$$d(X^T) = \sum (-1)^h x_{i_11} x_{i_22} \cdots x_{i_nn}$$
$$= \sum (-1)^{h'} x_{1i_1} x_{2i_2} \cdots x_{ni_n}$$

where h' is a number of transpositions into which the inverse of the substitution s can be factored. But h and h' are both even or both odd so that we have:

THEOREM 33. $d(A^T) = d(A)$.

Now let us replace the elements of the kth row of X by the sums

$$y_{k1} + z_{k1}, \ y_{k2} + z_{k2}, \ \cdots, \ y_{kn} + z_{kn},$$

denoting the new matrix by X'. Denote by Y the matrix obtained by replacing the kth row of X merely by the y's, and denote by Z the matrix obtained by replacing the kth row of X merely by the z's. Then

$$d(X') = \sum (-1)^h x_{1i_1} \cdots (y_{ki_k} + z_{ki_k}) \cdots x_{ni_n}$$
$$= \sum (-1)^h x_{1i_1} \cdots y_{ki_k} \cdots x_{ni_n}$$
$$+ \sum (-1)^h x_{1i_1} \cdots z_{ki_k} \cdots x_{ni_n}$$
$$= d(Y) + d(Z).$$

We have therefore proved

THEOREM 34. *If each element a_{ks} of the kth row of A is a sum*

$$b_{ks1} + b_{ks2} + \cdots + b_{ksm}$$

then

$$d(A) = d(A_1) + d(A_2) + \cdots + d(A_m)$$

where A_i differs from A only in that the elements in the kth row are b_{ksi} for $s = 1, 2, \cdots, n$. A similar result holds for columns.

22. Minors and cofactors. From the array

$$A = \begin{bmatrix} a_{11} & a_{12} & \cdots & a_{1n} \\ a_{21} & a_{22} & \cdots & a_{2n} \\ \cdot & \cdot & \cdot & \cdot & \cdot & \cdot & \cdot \\ a_{m1} & a_{m2} & \cdots & a_{mn} \end{bmatrix}$$

one can select certain rows and columns and thereby determine *subarrays* or *minors*. Thus if we select the elements common to the rows 3, 1, 4 and the columns 5, 3, we have the minor

$$A_{53}^{314} = \begin{bmatrix} a_{35} & a_{33} \\ a_{15} & a_{13} \\ a_{45} & a_{43} \end{bmatrix}.$$

If $A_{s_1 s_2 \cdots s_k}^{r_1 r_2 \cdots r_k}$ is square, its determinant is a *minor determinant* of A.

The following theorem is due to Laplace:

THEOREM 35.

$$d(A) = \sum \pm d(A_{i_1 i_2 \cdots i_k}^{r_1 r_2 \cdots r_k}) d(A_{i_{k+1} \cdots i_n}^{r_{k+1} \cdots r_n})$$

where the summation is over the $_nC_k$ ways of selecting the k numbers i_1, i_2, $\cdots$, i_k from among the numbers 1, 2, $\cdots$, n without regard for order, and the sign is $+$ or $-$ according as the substitution

$$\begin{pmatrix} r_1 & r_2 \cdots r_n \\ i_1 & i_2 \cdots i_n \end{pmatrix}$$

is even or odd.

The proof of this theorem is based upon the elementary fact that for every value of k all permutations of 1, 2, $\cdots$, n are obtained by separating 1, 2, $\cdots$, n into two unordered sets i_1, i_2, $\cdots$, i_k and i_{k+1}, $\cdots$, i_n in all possible ways, and then permuting each set in all possible ways. Details of the proof will be omitted.

23. Rank. We originally defined the row rank of a matrix A to be the number of linearly independent row vectors in the matrix (§11), and the column rank to be the number of linearly independent column vectors. Later (§14) these two numbers were shown to be equal, and were called the rank of the matrix.

Let ρ denote the order of a non-singular minor of A of maximum order. We shall now show that $\rho = r$, so that the rank of a matrix may be thus defined.

We assume that the column vectors

$$v_i = (a_{1i}, a_{2i}, \cdots, a_{ki}) \qquad (i = 1, 2, \cdots n)$$

of the matrix

$$A = \begin{bmatrix} a_{11} & a_{12} \cdots a_{1n} \\ a_{21} & a_{22} \cdots a_{2n} \\ \cdot & \cdot \cdot \cdot \cdot \cdot \cdot \\ a_{k1} & a_{k2} \cdots a_{kn} \end{bmatrix}$$

span a linear space of rank r. If there exists a non-singular minor of order ρ, we may assume the notation to be so chosen that

$$B = \begin{bmatrix} a_{11} & a_{12} \cdots a_{1\rho} \\ u_{21} & a_{22} \cdots a_{2\rho} \\ \cdot & \cdot \cdot \cdot \cdot \cdot \cdot \\ a_{\rho 1} & a_{\rho 2} \cdots a_{\rho \rho} \end{bmatrix}$$

is non-singular of determinant b. The vectors $v_1, v_2, \cdots,$ v_ρ are linearly independent, for a linear relation among them would imply a linear relation among the columns of B, and would therefore imply $b = 0$. Thus $r \geqq \rho$.

If $\rho = n$, then $r \leqq \rho$ and consequently $r = \rho$. If $\rho < n$, then every matrix

$$B_{lh} = \begin{bmatrix} a_{11} \cdots a_{1\rho} & a_{1h} \\ \cdot \cdot \cdot \cdot \cdot \cdot \cdot \cdot \\ a_{\rho 1} \cdots a_{\rho \rho} & a_{\rho h} \\ a_{l1} \cdots a_{l\rho} & a_{lh} \end{bmatrix} \quad \begin{array}{l} (h = \rho + 1, \cdots, n; \\ \\ l = 1, 2, \cdots, k) \end{array}$$

is singular. For $l \leqq \rho$, B_{lh} has two equal rows. For $l > \rho$, B_{lh} is a minor of A of order $\rho + 1$ and hence is singular by assumption. The cofactor of the element a_{ls} of the last row of B_{lh} is independent of l, and we may denote it by A_{hs}. Then by (19)

$$A_{h1}a_{l1} + A_{h2}a_{l2} + \cdots + A_{h\rho}a_{l\rho} + A_{hh}a_{lh} = 0.$$

Since this holds for $l = 1, 2, \cdots, k$,

$$A_{h1}v_1 + A_{h2}v_2 + \cdots + A_{h\rho}v_\rho + A_{hh}v_h = 0.$$

But $A_{hh} = b \neq 0$ so that every vector v_h, $h = \rho+1, \cdots, n$, is linearly dependent upon the vectors $v_1, v_2, \cdots, v_\rho$. Thus in every case $r \leq \rho$, and consequently $r = \rho$.

CHAPTER IV

MATRIC POLYNOMIALS

24. Ring with unit element. In modern abstract algebra it is customary to define a *ri ig* as a mathematical system consisting of elements and two operations called addition and multiplication, relative to which the system is closed, subject to the following postulates.

1. The system is a commutative group relative to addition, the identity element being denoted by 0, and the inverse of a by $-a$.

2. Multiplication is associative, i.e.,

$$(a \times b) \times c = a \times (b \times c).$$

3. Multiplication is distributive with respect to addition, i.e.,

$$a \times (b + c) = a \times b + a \times c,$$
$$(b + c) \times a = b \times a + c \times a.$$

Most rings which are of importance in mathematics are known as *rings with unit element*. In addition to the ring postulates they are subject to another postulate, namely

4. There exists an identity element 1 of multiplication such that

$$a \times 1 = 1 \times a = a$$

for every element a of the system.

The instances of ring with unit element are numerous and important. The rational numbers, the real numbers, the complex numbers, and in fact all fields are instances. So are the rational integers, the integers of an algebraic field, p-adic integers, etc. All of these rings possess commutative multiplication. Linear algebras which possess a unit element, and their sets of integral numbers, furnish instances of rings with unit element which are ordinarily not commutative.

Our particular interest in such rings lies in the fact that all $n \times n$ matrices whose elements lie in a ring with unit element themselves constitute a ring with unit element. This is not true of any more specialized mathematical system. That is, the coefficient ring in which the elements of the matrices lie may be commutative without the matric ring being commutative, and the coefficient ring may have the property that every non-zero element has an inverse with respect to multiplication without imparting this property to the matric ring.

25. Polynomial domains. Let us denote by R a ring with unit element 1. Let x be an indeterminate over this ring. The set of all polynomials in x with coefficients in R constitute a mathematical system $R[x]$ which is likewise a ring with unit element. This is called the *polynomial domain* of R. If R is commutative, so is $R[x]$.

It may be well to recall a few of the properties of indeterminates.* If

$$f(x) = a_0 + a_1 x + a_2 x^2, \qquad g(x) = b_0 + b_1 x + b_2 x^2$$

are two elements of $R[x]$, their sum is

$$f(x) + g(x) = (a_0 + b_0) + (a_1 + b_1)x + (a_2 + b_2)x^2,$$

and their product is

$$f(x) \cdot g(x) = a_0 b_0 + (a_1 b_0 + a_0 b_1)x + (a_2 b_0 + a_1 b_1 + a_0 b_2)x^2 \\ + (a_1 b_2 + a_2 b_1)x^3 + a_2 b_2 x^4.$$

* See the author's *An Introduction to Abstract Algebra*, Wiley, 1940, p. 158.

The indeterminate x is commutative with every number of R even when two numbers of R are not commutative with each other.

Let us for a moment suppose that R is commutative. Then $f(c)$ is a unique number of R, namely the number

$$a_0 + a_1c + a_2c^2$$

obtained by substituting c for the indeterminate x in the polynomial $f(x)$. From the equalities

$$f(x) + g(x) = h(x), \qquad f(x) \cdot g(x) = k(x)$$

in $R[x]$ follow the equalities

$$f(c) + g(c) = h(c), \qquad f(c) \cdot g(c) = k(c)$$

in R.

But if R is not commutative, it is not usually permissible to substitute a number of R for the indeterminate in every equality in $R[x]$. Thus in $R[x]$

$$\begin{aligned}
f(x) = a_0 + a_1x + a_2x^2 &= a_0 + xa_1 + x^2a_2 \\
= a_0 + a_1x + xa_2x &= a_0 + xa_1 + xa_2x \\
= a_0 + a_1x + x^2a_2 &= a_0 + xa_1 + x^2a_2.
\end{aligned}$$

The six numbers of R obtained by substituting a number c of R for x could well all be different. Thus let us take for R the ring of all two-rowed square matrices with rational elements. Let us take for $f(x)$ the polynomial

$$f(x) = \begin{bmatrix} 1 & 0 \\ 1 & 0 \end{bmatrix} x = x \begin{bmatrix} 1 & 0 \\ 1 & 0 \end{bmatrix}.$$

If we choose

$$c = \begin{bmatrix} 0 & 0 \\ 1 & 1 \end{bmatrix},$$

then

$$\begin{bmatrix} 1 & 0 \\ 1 & 0 \end{bmatrix} c = \begin{bmatrix} 0 & 0 \\ 0 & 0 \end{bmatrix}, \qquad c \begin{bmatrix} 1 & 0 \\ 1 & 0 \end{bmatrix} = \begin{bmatrix} 0 & 0 \\ 2 & 0 \end{bmatrix}.$$

Clearly the functional value $f(c)$ is not well defined.

Among all the possible functional values of a polynomial, two are of outstanding importance. Thus if

$$f(x) = a_0 + a_1 x + a_2 x^2 + \cdots + a_n x^n,$$

we define the *left functional value*

$$f_L(c) = a_0 + a_1 c + a_2 c^2 + \cdots + a_n c^n$$

to be the one where all coefficients are to the left of the powers of c, and similarly we define the *right functional value*

$$f_R(c) = a_0 + c a_1 + c^2 a_2 + \cdots + c^n a_n$$

where all the coefficients are on the right.

Even the restriction to left functional values does not immediately clear away the difficulties. Thus if

$$f(x) = a_0 + a_1 x, \qquad g(x) = b_0 + b_1 x,$$

$$f(x) \cdot g(x) = h(x) = a_0 b_0 + (a_0 b_1 + a_1 b_0) x + a_1 b_1 x^2,$$

$$f_L(c) \cdot g_L(c) = a_0 b_0 + a_0 b_1 c + a_1 c b_0 + a_1 c b_1 c,$$

which is in general different from

$$h_L(c) = a_0 b_0 + (a_0 b_1 + a_1 b_0) c + a_1 b_1 c^2.$$

It is hoped that the reader is now ready to admit that any orderly theorem which can be extracted from this chaos is worthy of consideration. The following theorem should not now appear trivial. That it is far from trivial will appear from its numerous applications.

THEOREM 36. *Let R be a ring with unit element, and let $R[x]$ be its polynomial domain. Let $f(x) \cdot g(x) = h(x)$ in*

$R[x]$. If $g_L(c) = 0$ in R, then $h_L(c) = 0$. If $f_R(c) = 0$ in R, then $h_R(c) = 0$.

We can show the method of proof as conclusively by using the polynomials given at the beginning of this section as in the general case. We have

$$h_L(c) = a_0b_0 + (a_1b_0 + a_0b_1)c + (a_2b_0 + a_1b_1 + a_0b_2)c^2$$
$$+ (a_1b_2 + a_2b_1)c^3 + a_2b_2c^4$$
$$= a_0 \cdot g_L(c) + a_1 \cdot g_L(c) \cdot c + a_2 \cdot g_L(c) \cdot c^2.$$

If $g_L(c) = 0$, then clearly $h_L(c) = 0$.

Similarly it is seen that
$$h_R(c) = f_R(c) \cdot b_0 + c \cdot f_R(c) \cdot b_1 + c^2 \cdot f_R(c) \cdot b_2$$

26. Degree of a polynomial. A number a of a ring R is called a *right divisor of zero* if there exists another element $a' \neq 0$ of the ring such that $a'a = 0$. According to this definition, 0 is a divisor of zero. A number $a \neq 0$ which is a right divisor of zero is called a *proper* right divisor of zero.

[unless the ring is the trivial ring containing only 0]

If a has a right inverse, it cannot be a right divisor of zero. For $a'a = 0$ would imply

$$(a'a)a^{-1} = a'(aa^{-1}) = a' = 0.$$

Similarly if a has a left inverse, it cannot be a left divisor of zero.

The concept of degree of a polynomial with coefficients in a ring with unit element is complicated not by the failure of the commutative law, which caused the difficulty in the last ~~paragraph~~ *section*, but by the possible existence of divisors of zero. We shall define the polynomial

$$f(x) = a_0 + a_1x + \cdots + a_{n-1}x^{n-1} + a_nx^n$$

to be of *degree n* if $a_n \neq 0$, to be of degree $n-1$ if $a_n = 0$ but $a_{n-1} \neq 0$, etc. If all the coefficients are 0, $f(x)$ has no degree. But to be useful this concept must be strengthened. A polynomial is of *proper* degree n if it is of degree n and if a_n has an inverse a_n^{-1} such that

$$a_n^{-1} a_n = a_n a_n^{-1} = 1.$$

In particular this will be the case if R is a ring of square matrices and if a_n is non-singular (§13). Clearly a_n cannot be a divisor of zero. If $a_n \neq 0$ but does not have a double inverse, $f(x)$ has no proper degree.

If $f(x)$ is of degree n and

$$g(x) = b_0 + b_1 x + \cdots + b_m x^m$$

is of degree m, then

$$f(x) \cdot g(x) = a_0 b_0 + \cdots + a_n b_m x^{m+n}.$$

Thus the degree of a product of two polynomials never exceeds the sum of their degrees. If $f(x)$ is of proper degree n, or if $g(x)$ is of proper degree m, then $f(x) \cdot g(x)$ is of degree exactly $m+n$. If both $f(x)$ and $g(x)$ are proper, so is their product, for

$$b_m^{-1} a_n^{-1} = (a_n b_m)^{-1}.$$

The following theorem is the analogue of the familiar "division algorithm."

THEOREM 37. *If $f(x)$ and $g(x)$ are polynomials of $R[x]$, and if $g(x)$ is of proper degree l, then unique polynomials $r(x)$ and $r_1(x)$ exist, each being 0 or of degree $<l$, and also unique polynomials $q(x)$ and $q_1(x)$, such that*

$$f(x) = q(x) \cdot g(x) + r(x), \quad f(x) = g(x) \cdot q_1(x) + r_1(x).$$

The proof is quite analogous to the proof of its elementary-algebra counterpart. Suppose, for instance, that

$$f(x) = a_0 + a_1x + a_2x^2 + a_3x^3, \quad g(x) = b_0 + b_1x + b_2x^2.$$

Since $g(x)$ is assumed to be of proper degree 2, b_2^{-1} exists in R. Then

$$f(x) - a_3b_2^{-1}x \cdot g(x)$$

is 0 or is a polynomial of degree at most 2 which we may denote by $d_0 + d_1x + d_2x^2$. Then

$$f(x) - a_3b_2^{-1}x \cdot g(x) - d_2b_2^{-1} \cdot g(x) = r(x)$$

is 0 or of degree < 2, and

$$f(x) = (a_3b_2^{-1}x + d_2b_2^{-1})g(x) + r(x),$$

thus establishing the existence of the $q(x)$ and $r(x)$ described in the theorem. By writing

$$f(x) = a_0 + xa_1 + x^2a_2 + x^3a_3$$

and working similarly on the other side, we can show the existence of $q_1(x)$ and $r_1(x)$. The method is quite general.

Suppose that

$$f(x) = q(x) \cdot g(x) + r(x) = q_2(x) \cdot g(x) + r_2(x)$$

where $r(x)$ is either 0 or of degree less than the degree l of $g(x)$, and similarly for $r_2(x)$. Then

$$(q(x) - q_2(x)) \cdot g(x) = r_2(x) - r(x).$$

Unless $q(x) - q_2(x)$ is 0, the left member of this equation is of degree $\geq l$, whereas the right member is 0 or of degree $< l$. Hence

$$q(x) - q_2(x) = 0, \qquad r_2(x) - r(x) = 0,$$

and the uniqueness of the $q(x)$ and $r(x)$ is proved.

THEOREM 38. *If there exist numbers c and d of R such that $g_L(c) = 0$, $g_R(d) = 0$ where $g(x)$ is described in Theorem 37, then*

$$f_L(c) = r_L(c), \qquad f_R(d) = r_{1R}(d),$$

respectively.

By Theorem 37,

$$h(x) = f(x) - r(x) = q(x) \cdot g(x).$$

By Theorem 36, $g_L(c) = 0$ implies $h_L(c) = 0$. But $h_L(c) = f_L(c) - r_L(c)$. The second part follows similarly.

As a special case of this theorem we have the Remainder Theorem:

COROLLARY 38. *If r is the remainder obtained by dividing $f(x)$ on the right by $x - c$, then $r = f_L(c)$. If r_1 is the remainder obtained by dividing $f(x)$ on the left by $x - c$, then $r_1 = f_R(c)$.*

Evidently $x - c$ is proper of degree 1 so that the r and r_1 of Theorem 38 are in R. If $g(x) = x - c$, then both $g_L(c)$ and $g_R(c)$ vanish.

27. Matrices with polynomial elements. If R is a ring with unit element, its polynomial domain $R[x]$ is likewise a ring with unit element. Let us consider a matrix with elements in $R[x]$ such as

$$A = \begin{bmatrix} 2x^3 + x^2 - x + 1 & x^2 + 2x + 2 \\ 3x^2 - x & x^3 + x + 3 \end{bmatrix}.$$

By the definitions of addition and scalar multiplication for matrices it is clear that

$$A = \begin{bmatrix} 2 & 0 \\ 0 & 1 \end{bmatrix} x^3 + \begin{bmatrix} 1 & 1 \\ 3 & 0 \end{bmatrix} x^2 + \begin{bmatrix} -1 & 2 \\ -1 & 1 \end{bmatrix} x + \begin{bmatrix} 1 & 2 \\ 0 & 3 \end{bmatrix}.$$

Here x is an indeterminate defined over the ring R.

On the other hand, one can look upon the last expression for A as a polynomial whose coefficients are matrices with elements in R. In that case x must be considered as an indeterminate defined over the ring of two-rowed matrices with elements in R. Clearly it makes no difference which of these points of view we take. That is, the polynomial domain of the total matric algebra of order n^2 over R is isomorphic with the total matric algebra of order n^2 over $R[x]$.

28. The characteristic function. Let $A = (a_{rs})$ be an $n \times n$ matrix with elements in a field F. It is evident that A satisfies an equation of degree $\leq n^2$ with coefficients in F. For the condition

$$a_0 I + a_1 A + a_2 A^2 + \cdots + a_{n^2} A^{n^2} = 0$$

is equivalent to n^2 homogeneous equations in the $n^2 + 1$ unknown coefficients, and such a system of equations always has a non-trivial solution, by Corollary 4.

But a much stronger relation than this holds, for the matrix A actually satisfies an equation of degree $\leq n$ with coefficients in F. This fact is not at all obvious.

The matrix $Ix - A$ is non-singular in the field of all rational functions of x, for its rows are linearly independent. Thus for $n = 3$, the row-vectors

$$v_1 = (x - a_{11}, \quad - a_{12}, \quad - a_{13}),$$
$$v_2 = (\quad - a_{21}, \; x - a_{22}, \quad - a_{23}),$$
$$v_3 = (\quad - a_{31}, \quad - a_{32}, \; x - a_{33})$$

are independent. For if there were a linear relation

$$c_1 v_1 + c_2 v_2 + c_3 v_3 = 0,$$

it could be assumed without loss of generality that c_1, c_2, c_3 were polynomials. If not all of them were zero, we could choose one, say c_2, which was of maximal degree d. Then

$$c_2(x - a_{22}) = c_1 a_{12} + c_3 a_{32}.$$

But the left member of this equation is of degree $d+1$, while the right member is of degree at most d. Thus we are forced to conclude that $c_1 = c_2 = c_3 = 0$, and that v_1, v_2, v_3 are linearly independent.

The linear matric polynomial $Ix - A$ can be written as a matrix whose elements are constants or linear polynomials in the indeterminate x. This matrix has an adjoint which is a matrix whose non-zero elements are polynomials in x of degree $n-1$ or less. This adjoint can now be written in the form

$$\text{adj } (Ix - A) = C_0 + C_1 x + \cdots + C_{n-1} x^{n-1}$$

where the coefficients are $n \times n$ matrices with elements in F. By (20)

$$(21) \qquad \text{adj } (Ix - A) \cdot (Ix - A) = d(Ix - A) \cdot I.$$

The determinant $d(Ix - A)$ is a polynomial of degree n with coefficients in F, which we shall denote by $f(x)$ and call the *characteristic function* of A. Then $f(x) \cdot I$ may also be regarded as a polynomial in x with coefficients in the ring of $n \times n$ matrices with elements in F. Evidently the matric polynomial $Ix - A$ becomes 0 when A is substituted for x, so by Theorem 36, the polynomial

$$d(Ix - A) \cdot I = f(x) \cdot I$$

also vanishes when x is replaced by A. Since $f(x)$ has scalar coefficients, the left and right functional values are the same. Since $f(x) \cdot I$ may also be regarded as a scalar matrix whose diagonal elements are the polynomials $f(x)$, it follows from $f(A) \cdot I = 0$ that $f(A) = 0$. We have therefore proved the important Hamilton-Cayley Theorem:

THEOREM 39. *Every matrix A satisfies its character-istic equation*

$$f(x) = d(Ix - A) = 0.$$

29. The minimum function. Since every $n \times n$ matrix A with elements in F satisfies an equation with coefficients in F, it is evident that it satisfies such an equation of lowest possible degree. The degree μ of such an equation is called the *index* of A. The Hamilton-Cayley Theorem tells us that $\mu \leqq n$. If $\mu < n$, A is called *derogatory*. That derogatory matrices exist is demonstrated by the fact that scalar matrices satisfy equations of the first degree. (The scalar matrix A satisfies the eq. $f(x) = x - a =$ $\begin{bmatrix} a & 0 \\ 0 & a \end{bmatrix}$ since $A - aI = 0$)

Now let

$$m(x) = x^\mu + m_1 x^{\mu-1} + \cdots + m_\mu = 0$$

be an equation with coefficients in F of minimum degree μ satisfied by the matrix A. The function $m(x)$ has been chosen with leading coefficient equal to 1. If $g(x) = 0$ is any equation with coefficients in F such that $g(A) = 0$, we can write

$$g(x) = q(x) \cdot m(x) + r(x)$$

where $r(x)$ is 0 or of degree $< \mu$. But $g(A) = 0$ and $m(A) = 0$, so that $r(A) = 0$ by Theorem 38. Since no polynomial of degree $< \mu$ such that $r(A) = 0$ exists, it follows that $r(x) = 0$ and $m(x)$ is a divisor of $g(x)$. We have proved

THEOREM 40. *The minimum function of a matrix A with elements in F is unique up to a non-zero constant factor. If $g(x)$ is any polynomial with coefficients in F such that $g(A) = 0$, then $g(x)$ is divisible by the minimum function of A.*

As we have seen,

$$\text{adj}\,(Ix - A) \cdot (Ix - A) = f(x) \cdot I.$$

If the elements of $\text{adj}(Ix - A)$ have a greatest common divisor of degree > 0, this polynomial will be a divisor of every element of the left member of the above equation and will therefore be a divisor of $f(x)$. We shall venture to define the quotient of $\text{adj}(Ix - A)$ by that greatest common divisor of its elements whose leading coefficient is 1 as the *supplement* of $Ix - A$, and to write it as $\sup(Ix - A)$. Its elements are relatively prime polynomials in x, and it satisfies an equation

$$(22) \qquad \sup\,(Ix - A) \cdot (Ix - A) = h(x) \cdot I$$

where $h(x)$ is a divisor of the characteristic polynomial $f(x)$ and has 1 as its leading coefficient.

THEOREM 41. *The polynomial $h(x)$ is the minimum function of A.*

The proof that $h(A) = 0$ follows from (22) by the same argument that was used in the proof of Theorem 39. Hence $m(x)$ divides $h(x)$ by Theorem 40, so that we may write

$$h(x) = k(x) \cdot m(x).$$

Let $g(x)$ be any polynomial with coefficients in F such that $g(A) = 0$. By the division algorithm (Theorem 37) there exists a matric polynomial $P(x)$ and a matrix Q with scalar elements such that

$$g(x) \cdot I = P(x) \cdot (xI - A) + Q.$$

By Corollary 38, $Q = g(A) \cdot I = 0$ so that

$$g(x) \cdot I = P(x) \cdot (xI - A).$$

Now $m(x)$ is a polynomial which vanishes for $x = A$.

Set

(23) $$m(x) \cdot I = P(x) \cdot (xI - A).$$

[margin note: since in the above g(x) is any polynomial with coeffs. in F such that g(A) is 0. m(x) is such a polynomial.]

Then by (22)

$$\sup (Ix - A) \cdot (Ix - A) = k(x) \cdot P(x) \cdot (Ix - A).$$

Since $Ix - A$ is non-singular,

$$\sup (Ix - A) = k(x) \cdot P(x).$$

That is, every element of the matrix $\sup(Ix - A)$ is divisible by the scalar polynomial $k(x)$. But the elements of $\sup(Ix - A)$ are relatively prime polynomials so that $k(x)$ is a non-zero constant. Since both $m(x)$ and $h(x)$ have leading coefficient 1, they are equal.

THEOREM 42. *The distinct factors of the characteristic function $f(x)$ of A which are irreducible in F coincide with the distinct factors of the minimum function $m(x)$ which are irreducible in F.*

Since $m(x)$ divides $f(x)$, every irreducible factor of $m(x)$ occurs in $f(x)$. From (23) we have, by taking the determinant of each member,

$$[m(x)]^n = d(P(x)) \cdot f(x).$$

Consequently each irreducible factor of $f(x)$ occurs as a factor of $m(x)$.

COROLLARY 42. *If the characteristic function of A is a product of distinct irreducible factors, then A is not derogatory.*

30. The rank of a polynomial in a matrix. If A is a matrix of order n and rank $r \leq n$ with minimum function $m(x)$, the polynomial $m(A)$ is of rank 0. The question arises whether there are other polynomials in A with scalar coefficients whose ranks are less than n but greater than 0.

THEOREM 43. *Let the matrix A have the minimum function $m(x)$. Let $f(x)$ be any polynomial with scalar coefficients, and let $d(x)$ be the greatest common divisor of $m(x)$ and $f(x)$. Then the rank of $f(A)$ is equal to the rank of $d(A)$.*

Since $d(x)$ is a divisor of $f(x)$, there exists a polynomial $k(x)$ such that $f(x) = k(x) \cdot d(x)$. Then

$$f(A) = k(A) \cdot d(A),$$

whence it follows by Theorem 14 that the rank of $f(A)$ is less than or equal to the rank of $d(A)$.

Since $d(x)$ is a greatest common divisor of $m(x)$ and $f(x)$, there exist polynomials $p(x)$ and $q(x)$ such that[*]

$$d(x) = p(x) \cdot m(x) + q(x) \cdot f(x).$$

Then, since $m(A) = 0$,

$$d(A) = q(A) \cdot f(A).$$

Again from Theorem 14 it follows that the rank of $d(A)$ is less than or equal to the rank of $f(A)$. Thus $d(A)$ and $f(A)$ have the same rank.

THEOREM 44. *The matrix $f(A)$ is singular if and only if $f(x)$ has a factor of degree ≥ 1 in common with the minimum function of A.*

Let $d(x)$ be any divisor of degree ≥ 1 of the minimum function $m(x)$ of A. Let $m(x) = k(x) \cdot d(x)$. Then

$$0 = m(A) = k(A) \cdot d(A).$$

But $k(A)$ is of rank greater than 0, for $k(x)$ is of lower degree than the minimum function $m(x)$. If $d(A)$ were non-

and therefo
$k(A) \neq 0$

---

* See, for instance, L. Weisner, *Introduction to the Theory of Equations*, Macmillan, 1938, p. 30.

singular, the product $k(A) \cdot d(A)$ would likewise be of rank greater than 0, by Theorem 17. Thus $d(A)$ is singular.

If $f(x)$ has a greatest common divisor $d(x)$ of degree $\geqq 1$ in common with $m(x)$, then $f(A)$ has the same rank as $d(A)$ by Theorem 43, and hence is singular. If $f(x)$ is relatively prime to $m(x)$, their greatest common divisor is $d(x) = 1$, so that $d(A) = I$, which is of rank n. Hence $f(x)$ is non-singular.

31. Matrix having a given minimum function. Let

$$m(x) = a_0 + a_1 x + a_2 x^2 + x^3$$

be a given polynomial with coefficients in a field. We have assumed that the degree of the polynomial is 3, but the argument applies equally well to a polynomial of any degree. It is no restriction to assume that the leading coefficient is 1.

Consider the matrix

$$A = \begin{bmatrix} 0 & 0 & -a_0 \\ 1 & 0 & -a_1 \\ 0 & 1 & -a_2 \end{bmatrix}.$$

which has the negatives of the coefficients of $m(x)$ in the last column, 1's in the diagonal just below the main diagonal, and 0's elsewhere. Evidently

$$d(Ix - A) = \begin{bmatrix} x & 0 & a_0 \\ -1 & x & a_1 \\ 0 & -1 & x + a_2 \end{bmatrix}.$$

If we add to the second row x times the third row, the determinant is not changed (Theorem 32). That is,

$$d(Ix - A) = \begin{bmatrix} x & 0 & a_0 \\ -1 & 0 & x^2 + a_2x + a_1 \\ 0 & -1 & x + a_2 \end{bmatrix}.$$

Now add to the first row x times the second row.

$$d(Ix - A) = \begin{bmatrix} 0 & 0 & x^3 + a_2x^2 + a_1x + a_0 \\ -1 & 0 & x^2 + a_2x + a_1 \\ 0 & -1 & x + a_2 \end{bmatrix}.$$

Now expand by the Laplace expansion in terms of the elements of the first row (Theorem 35).

$$d(Ix - A) = x^3 + a_2x^2 + a_1x + a_0 = m(x).$$

Thus the matrix A has $m(x)$ as its characteristic polynomial.

We may see that $m(x)$ is also the minimum polynomial of A. Evidently the $(n-1)$-rowed minor determinant in the lower left-hand corner of $d(Ix-A)$ is equal to ± 1, so that the $(n-1)$-rowed minor determinants are relatively prime polynomials. But these polynomials are the elements of adj$(Ix-A)$. It now follows from (22) that

$$\text{adj } (Ix - A) = \sup (Ix - A)$$

so that the minimum polynomial $m(x)$ coincides with the characteristic polynomial $f(x)$.

We shall call A the *companion matrix* of its minimum equation.

32. The norm. By setting $x = 0$ in the equation

$$d(Ix - A) = f(x),$$

we see that the constant term of the characteristic function $f(x)$ multiplied by $(-1)^n$ is equal to the determinant of A. If

$$m(x) = x^\mu + m_1 x^{\mu-1} + \cdots + m_\mu$$

is the minimum function of A, we shall define $(-1)^\mu m_\mu$ to be the *norm* of A, written $n(A)$.

THEOREM 45. *The norm of A is 0 if and only if A is singular.*

For by Theorem 44 A is singular if and only if x divides $m(x)$, in which case $m_\mu = 0$.

Let us write the minimum function of a matrix $A \neq 0$ as

$$m(x) = x^\mu + m_1 x^{\mu-1} + \cdots + m_{\mu-1} x \pm n(A).$$

Since $m(A) = 0$,

$$A(A^{\mu-1} + m_1 A^{\mu-2} + \cdots + m_{\mu-1})$$
$$= (A^{\mu-1} + m_1 A^{\mu-2} + \cdots + m_{\mu-1})A = \pm n(A).$$

The matrix in parenthesis cannot be 0 for $m(x)$, the minimum polynomial, was of degree μ. Hence if $n(A) = 0$, A is both a left and a right proper divisor of zero. If $n(A) \neq 0$,

$$\frac{A(A^{\mu-1} + m_1 A^{\mu-2} + \cdots + m_{\mu-1})}{\pm n(A)} = I$$

so that

$$A^{-1} = \frac{A^{\mu-1} + m_1 A^{\mu-2} + \cdots + m_{\mu-1}}{\pm n(A)}.$$

Hence A has a left and right inverse and cannot be a left or a right divisor of zero. We have therefore proved

THEOREM 46. *A matrix $A \neq 0$ is a proper left and right divisor of zero if and only if it is singular. If A is singular, there exists a polynomial $m_1(x)$ of degree $\mu - 1$ such that*

$$m_1(A) \cdot A = A \cdot m_1(A) = 0.$$

If A is non-singular, its inverse can be written as a polynomial in A.

We illustrate with a numerical example. Let

$$A = \begin{bmatrix} 7 & 4 & -1 \\ 4 & 7 & -1 \\ -4 & -4 & 4 \end{bmatrix}.$$

Let the characteristic function be

$$d(Ix - A) = f(x) = x^3 + a_2 x^2 + a_1 x + a_0.$$

Then a_2 is the negative of the sum of the diagonal elements, a_1 is the sum of the two-rowed minor determinants which are symmetrically placed with respect to the principal diagonal, and a_0 is the negative of the determinant. That is,

$$a_2 = - (7 + 7 + 4) = - 18,$$

$$a_1 = \begin{vmatrix} 7 & 4 \\ 4 & 7 \end{vmatrix} + \begin{vmatrix} 7 & -1 \\ -4 & 4 \end{vmatrix} + \begin{vmatrix} 7 & -1 \\ -4 & 4 \end{vmatrix} = 81,$$

$$a_0 = - \begin{vmatrix} 7 & 4 & -1 \\ 4 & 7 & -1 \\ -4 & -4 & 4 \end{vmatrix} = - 108.$$

Thus

$$f(x) = x^3 - 18x^2 + 81x - 108 = (x - 3)^2 (x - 12).$$

Since $f(x)$ has a repeated factor, it is worth while to

see if A is derogatory. The only possibility for $m(x)$, other than to equal $f(x)$, is

$$m(x) = (x - 3)(x - 12),$$

since $m(x)$ and $f(x)$ have the same distinct irreducible factors by Theorem 42. Now

$$(A-3I)(A-12I) = \begin{bmatrix} 4 & 4 & -1 \\ 4 & 4 & -1 \\ -4 & -4 & 1 \end{bmatrix}\begin{bmatrix} -5 & 4 & -1 \\ 4 & -5 & -1 \\ -4 & -4 & -8 \end{bmatrix} = 0,$$

so the minimum function is

$$m(x) = x^2 - 15x + 36 = x(x - 15) + 36.$$

Then the inverse of A is

$$A^{-1} = \frac{A - 15I}{-36} = \frac{-1}{36}\begin{bmatrix} -8 & 4 & -1 \\ 4 & -8 & -1 \\ -4 & -4 & -11 \end{bmatrix}.$$

We shall conclude the chapter with

COROLLARY 46. *If $f(x)$ is relatively prime to the minimum function of A, then $f(A)$ has an inverse $f^{-1}(A)$ which is a polynomial in A.*

By Theorem 44 $f(A)$ is non-singular. By Theorem 46 its inverse can be written as a polynomial in $f(A)$, and consequently as a polynomial in A.

CHAPTER V

UNION AND INTERSECTION

33. Complementary spaces. Two vectors

$$\alpha = (a_1, a_2, \cdots, a_n), \qquad \phi = (v_1, v_2, \cdots, v_n)$$

of the total vector space S of dimension n are said to be *orthogonal* if their inner product vanishes—that is, if

$$\alpha \cdot \phi = a_1 v_1 + a_2 v_2 + \cdots + a_n v_n = 0.$$

If ϕ is orthogonal to each of the vectors α and β, then

$$(k_1 \alpha + k_2 \beta) \cdot \phi = k_1 \alpha \cdot \phi + k_2 \beta \cdot \phi = 0,$$

so that ϕ is orthogonal to every vector of the form $k_1 \alpha + k_2 \beta$. In general, if ϕ is orthogonal to any number of vectors $\alpha, \beta, \cdots$, it is orthogonal to every vector of the linear system (§7) S_1 which they define. We then say that ϕ is orthogonal to the linear system S_1, and write

$$S_1 \cdot \phi = 0.$$

Now consider the set S_1' of all vectors $\phi, \chi, \cdots$ which are orthogonal to the linear system S_1. Then

$$S_1 \cdot (k_1 \phi + k_2 \chi + \cdots) = k_1 S_1 \cdot \phi + k_2 S_1 \cdot \chi + \cdots = 0$$

so that $k_1 \phi + k_2 \chi + \cdots$ is in S_1'. Thus the set S_1' is a linear system of vectors. We call S_1' the *orthogonal complement** of S_1.

---

* When S_1 is a real Euclidean space, S_1' is its orthogonal complement in the sense in which geometers use the term. But the reader should be warned not to look for a similar geometric interpretation in general. Thus if F is the complex field a vector such as $(i, 0, 1)$ may be in both S_1 and S_1'.

According to Theorem 8, S_1 has a basis of the form

$$\alpha_1 = (a_{11}, 0, \cdots, 0), \quad \alpha_2 = (a_{21}, a_{22}, \cdots, 0),$$
$$\cdots, \alpha_n = (a_{n1}, a_{n2}, \cdots, a_{nn})$$

where it is understood that either $a_{ii} \neq 0$ or else α_i is not present. If $\chi = (x_1, x_2, \cdots, x_n)$ is a vector of S_1', then

$$(25) \quad \begin{aligned} a_{11}x_1 &= 0, \\ a_{21}x_1 + a_{22}x_2 &= 0, \\ a_{31}x_1 + a_{32}x_2 + a_{33}x_3 &= 0, \\ &\cdots \\ a_{n1}x_1 + a_{n2}x_2 + \cdots + a_{nn}x_n &= 0. \end{aligned}$$

If $a_{11} \neq 0$, then $x_1 = 0$. If $a_{22} \neq 0$, x_2 is a multiple of x_1. In general if $a_{ii} \neq 0$, x_i is a definite linear combination of $x_1, x_2, \cdots, x_{i-1}$. On the other hand, if $a_{ii} = 0$, x_i is completely arbitrary. If S_1 is of rank r, exactly $n-r$ equations are missing, $n-r$ of the x_i are arbitrary, and the other x_i's are definite linear combinations of these. Thus the linear system S_1' can be written

$$\chi = x_{i_1}\phi_{i_1} + x_{i_2}\phi_{i_2} + \cdots + x_{i_{n-r}}\phi_{i_{n-r}}$$

where the ϕ's are vectors whose components are fixed numbers of the field, while the x_i's are arbitrary. Moreover, the ϕ's are linearly independent, since each ϕ_{i_j} has a 1 in the i_j-th position and 0's in each preceding position. Thus we have proved

THEOREM 47. *If the linear system S_1' of rank r' is the orthogonal complement of the linear system S_1 of rank r, then*

$$r + r' = n.$$

It is clear that ϕ_{ij} cannot be a lin. comb. of only some of the succeeding ϕ_i for ϕ_{ij} has a 1 as the i_j-th component while succeeding ϕ_i have 0 as the i_j-th component. (among others)

Furthermore ϕ_{ij} cannot be a lin. comb. of some of the preceding ϕ_i for this would imply that the first of the preceding ϕ would be a lin. comb. of only succeeding ϕ_i, contradicting 1).

then α_i and the i-th equation of (25) are not present

Thus if k is included in the i_j's all the vectors before and after ϕ_i have 0 as k-th comp.; ϕ_{i_k} has 1 for k-th comp.

If k is not in the i_j's all vectors after ϕ_{i_g} where $i_g = $ last $i_j \geq k$ have 0 for k-th component of χ. So that χ_k will be linear comb. of only the χ_i for $i < k$.

suppose $i_1 = 1, i_2 = 3$. Then χ has its 1st and 3rd component arbitrary, i.e. x_1 and x_3, respectively. Hence ϕ_{i_1} has a 1 as its 1st component, all other vectors ϕ_i have 0 for the 1st component; ϕ_{i_2} has 1 for its 3rd component; all other vectors ϕ_i have 0 for the 3rd component. The 2nd component of χ is a linear combination of the preceding components of χ (i.e. the 1st) — hence all the ϕ_i from ϕ_{i_2} onward have 0 for the second component.

We defined S_1' to be the set of all vectors orthogonal to every vector of S_1. It is now evident that S_1 is likewise the orthogonal complement of S_1'. For clearly the orthogonal complement S_1'' of S_1' contains S_1, and since S_1 and S_1'' are both of rank $n - r'$, they coincide.

By way of illustration, let us suppose that S_1 has the basis

$$\alpha_2 = (2, 1, 0, 0), \qquad \alpha_4 = (-1, 2, 3, 1).$$

Equations (25) become

$$2x_1 + x_2 \qquad\qquad = 0,$$
$$- x_1 + 2x_2 + 3x_3 + x_4 = 0.$$

Since α_1 and α_3 are missing, x_1 and x_3 are arbitrary, and

$$x_2 = -2x_1, \qquad x_4 = x_1 - 2x_2 - 3x_3 = 5x_1 - 3x_3.$$

Then

$$\begin{aligned}
\chi &= (x_1, x_2, x_3, x_4) = (x_1, -2x_1, x_3, 5x_1 - 3x_3) \\
&= x_1(1, -2, 0, 5) + x_3(0, 0, 1, -3) \\
&= x_1\phi_1 + x_3\phi_3.
\end{aligned}$$

The vector ϕ_3 has a 1 in the third place and 0's in the first two places. Clearly $\chi = 0$ implies $x_1 = x_3 = 0$, so that ϕ_1 and ϕ_3 are linearly independent and form a basis for the space S_1' complementary to S_1. Then S_1' is of rank 2.

34. Linear homogeneous systems.

The problem of finding the general solution of a system of linear homogeneous equations is essentially the problem of finding the orthogonal complement of the linear system of vectors determined by the coefficients of the given equations. Consider the system of equations

$$
\begin{aligned}
a_{11}x_1 + a_{12}x_2 + \cdots + a_{1n}x_n &= 0,\\
a_{21}x_1 + a_{22}x_2 + \cdots + a_{2n}x_n &= 0,\\
\cdot\ \cdot\ \cdot\ \cdot\ \cdot\ \cdot\ \cdot\ \cdot\ \cdot\ \cdot\ \cdot\ &\cdot\ \cdot\\
a_{k1}x_1 + a_{k2}x_2 + \cdots + a_{kn}x_n &= 0,
\end{aligned}
$$

(26)

and denote by α_i the vector

$$(a_{i1},\ a_{i2},\ \cdots,\ a_{in}).$$

The vectors $\alpha_1,\ \alpha_2,\ \cdots,\ \alpha_k$ determine a linear vector system S_1. The set of all vectors $\chi = (x_1,\ x_2,\ \cdots,\ x_n)$ which satisfy (26) constitute the orthogonal complement S_1' of S_1.

If the matrix of the equations (26) is of rank r, then S_1 is of rank r, and S_1' is of rank $n - r$. The space S_1' has a basis composed of $n - r$ linearly independent vectors. Such a basis of S_1' is called a *fundamental system of solutions* of the equations (26), for each vector of the basis is a solution of (26), and every solution of (26) is a linear combination of them.

Directly from Corollary 9c of the Steinitz Replacement Theorem we have

THEOREM 48. *A set of solutions of* (26) *is a fundamental system provided it consists of* $n - r$ *linearly independent solutions.*

Let A be any matrix of n columns of rank r. Its row vectors are the coefficients of a system of equations (26). Let X be a matrix whose row vectors constitute a fundamental system of solutions of these equations. Then X is of rank $n - r$, and

$$AX^T = 0.$$

We shall define a matrix X to be an *orthogonal com-*

plement of a matrix A if both A and X have n columns, if the sum of their ranks is n, and if $AX^T = 0$.

If $AX^T = 0$, then $XA^T = 0$, so that A is also an orthogonal complement of X.

The orthogonal complement is not unique, for if X spans S_1', so does QX where Q is any non-singular matrix. Moreover, A may be replaced by PA where P is any non-singular matrix without disturbing the solution matrix X. That is, the equations of (26) may be subjected to any elementary row transformation which may be useful in simplifying them.

Consider the equations

$$4x + 8y + 18z + 7w = 0,$$
$$4y + 10z + w = 0,$$
$$10x + 18y + 40z + 17w = 0,$$
$$x + 7y + 17z + 3w = 0.$$

We have

$$A = \begin{bmatrix} 4 & 8 & 18 & 7 \\ 0 & 4 & 10 & 1 \\ 10 & 18 & 40 & 17 \\ 1 & 7 & 17 & 3 \end{bmatrix}.$$

This matrix is of rank 2, and it may readily be verified that

$$X = \begin{bmatrix} 5 & 1 & 0 & -4 \\ 13 & 0 & 1 & -10 \end{bmatrix}$$

is an orthogonal complement.

35. Union and intersection. Let us denote by S the total vector space of dimension—that is, rank—n. Thus S consists of all vectors

$$\alpha = (a_1, a_2, \cdots, a_n)$$

whose components are in F. We may choose for S a basis

$$(1, 0, \cdots, 0), (0, 1, \cdots, 0), \cdots, (0, 0, \cdots, 1),$$

so that S is spanned by the row vectors of the identity matrix I.

A *linear subsystem* or *linear subspace* S_1 of S is a linear system of vectors all of which belong to S. We write $S_1 \subseteq S$. If not every vector of S is in S_1, S_1 is a *proper* subspace of S, and we write $S_1 \subset S$. If $S_1 \subset S$, it must be true that S_1 is of lower rank than S. For if they were of the same rank n, each would have a basis composed of n linearly independent vectors. Each vector of the basis of S_1 would equal a linear combination of the basic vectors of S. Hence by Corollary 9c, the basis of S_1 would be a basis for S, so that S and S_1 would coincide.

If S_1 and S_2 are linear subspaces of S, we define their *union* $S_1 \cup S_2$ to be the set of all vectors $\alpha + \beta$ where α ranges over S_1 and β ranges over S_2. The union is a linear subspace of S. For if γ_1 and γ_2 are any two vectors of $S_1 \cup S_2$,

$$\gamma_1 = \alpha_1 + \beta_1, \qquad \gamma_2 = \alpha_2 + \beta_2$$

where α_1 and α_2 are in S_1, and β_1 and β_2 are in S_2. Then for any two numbers k and l of F,

$$k\gamma_1 + l\gamma_2 = (k\alpha_1 + l\alpha_2) + (k\beta_1 + l\beta_2).$$

Since S_1 is a linear space, $k\alpha_1 + l\alpha_2$ is in S_1, and since S_2 is a linear space, $k\beta_1 + l\beta_2$ is in S_2. Thus $k\gamma_1 + l\gamma_2$ is in $S_1 \cup S_2$.

If the vectors $\alpha_1, \alpha_2, \cdots, \alpha_p$ span S_1 and the vectors $\beta_1, \beta_2, \cdots, \beta_q$ span S_2, then the vectors

$$\alpha_1, \alpha_2, \cdots, \alpha_p, \beta_1, \beta_2, \cdots, \beta_q$$

span $S_1 \cup S_2$. If S_1 is of rank r_1 and S_2 is of rank r_2, the union contains at most $r_1 + r_2$ linearly independent vectors, and at least as many as the greater of r_1 and r_2. Thus we have

THEOREM 49. *The rank (or dimension) of $S_1 \cup S_2$ is at least as great as the greater of the ranks of S_1 and S_2, and at most as great as the sum of their ranks.*

If S_1 and S_2 are linear subspaces of S, we define their *intersection* $S_1 \cap S_2$ to be the set of all vectors which are in both S_1 and S_2. The intersection is a linear subspace of S. For if γ_1 and γ_2 are any two vectors of $S_1 \cap S_2$,

$$\gamma = k\gamma_1 + l\gamma_2$$

is in S_1 since S_1 is a linear space, and γ is in S_2 since S_2 is a linear space, so that γ is in $S_1 \cap S_2$.

Let $S_1 \cap S_2$ be of rank m, S_1 of rank r_1, and S_2 of rank r_2. Let $S_1 \cap S_2$ have a basis

$$\gamma_1, \gamma_2, \cdots, \gamma_m.$$

Since these vectors are linearly independent and are in both S_1 and S_2, there exists a basis of S_1 of the form

$$\gamma_1, \gamma_2, \cdots, \gamma_m, \alpha_{m+1}, \cdots, \alpha_{r_1},$$

and there exists a basis of S_2 of the form

$$\gamma_1, \gamma_2, \cdots, \gamma_m, \beta_{m+1}, \cdots, \beta_{r_2}.$$

This is needed before cor. 9d is applied.

This follows immediately from Corollary 9d. ~~Thus~~

$$r_1 \geqq m, \qquad r_2 \geqq m.$$

Evidently the vectors

$$(27) \quad \gamma_1, \gamma_2, \cdots, \gamma_m, \alpha_{m+1}, \cdots, \alpha_{r_1}, \beta_{m+1}, \cdots, \beta_{r_2}$$

span the union $S_1 \cup S_2$. As a matter of fact, these vectors are linearly independent and hence constitute a basis for the union. For suppose that there existed a linear relation

$$k_1\gamma_1 + \cdots + k_m\gamma_m + k_{m+1}\alpha_{m+1} + \cdots + k_{r_1}\alpha_{r_1}$$
$$+ l_{m+1}\beta_{m+1} + \cdots + l_{r_2}\beta_{r_2} = 0.$$

If some l_i were not zero, then because of the linear independence of the β's,

$$l_{m+1}\beta_{m+1} + \cdots + l_{r_2}\beta_{r_2}$$
$$= -k_1\gamma_1 - \cdots - k_m\gamma_m - k_{m+1}\alpha_{m+1} - \cdots - k_{r_1}\alpha_{r_1}$$

would be a vector $\neq 0$ in both S_2 and S_1 and therefore in $S_1 \cap S_2$. It would then equal a linear combination of $\gamma_1, \gamma_2, \cdots, \gamma_m$. This would imply a linear relation among the basic vectors of S_2, which is impossible. Thus every $l_i = 0$. Now a relation

i.e. $l_{m+1}\beta_{m+1} + \cdots + l_{r_2}\beta_{r_2}$ — lin comb. of $\gamma_1, \gamma_2, \cdots, \gamma_m = 0$ without all the l_i being zero.

$$k_1\gamma_1 + \cdots + k_m\gamma_m + k_{m+1}\alpha_{m+1} + \cdots + k_{r_1}\alpha_{r_1} = 0$$

would imply a dependence among the basic vectors of S_1 unless every $k_i = 0$. Thus the vectors (27) are linearly independent, and the rank of $S_1 \cup S_2$ is $r_1 + r_2 - m$.

Let us denote the rank (dimension) of the linear subspace S_1 by $r(S_1)$. We have proved the following theorem:

THEOREM 50. $r(S_1) + r(S_2) = r(S_1 \cap S_2) + r(S_1 \cup S_2)$.

The concepts of union and intersection apply to any number of subspaces

$$S_1, S_2, \cdots, S_k$$

of S. The *union*, which may be written in either of the notations

$$S_1 \cup S_2 \cup \cdots \cup S_k, \qquad (S_1, S_2, \cdots, S_k)$$

is composed of all vectors of S which can be written as a sum

$$\alpha_1 + \alpha_2 + \cdots + \alpha_k$$

where α_i ranges over all vectors of S_i. The *intersection*

$$S_1 \cap S_2 \cap \cdots \cap S_k = [S_1, S_2, \cdots, S_k]$$

is composed of all vectors which are common to all the subspaces S_1, S_2, $\cdots$, S_k. Both the union and the intersection are linear subspaces of S, and both operations $\cup$ and $\cap$ are associative and commutative.

THEOREM 51. *Denote by* S_i' *the orthogonal complement of* S_i, *and let*

$$D = (S_1, S_2, \cdots, S_k), \qquad M = [S_1, S_2, \cdots, S_k],$$
$$D' = (S_1', S_2', \cdots, S_k'), \qquad M' = [S_1', S_2', \cdots, S_k'].$$

Then M' *is the orthogonal complement of* D, *and* M *is the orthogonal complement of* D'.

Let ϕ be any vector of the orthogonal complement of D. Since every vector α_i of S_i is in D, it is true that $\alpha_i \cdot \phi = 0$ so that ϕ is in S_i' for every i, and consequently is in M'.

Now let ϕ be any vector of M', and let

$$\alpha = \alpha_1 + \alpha_2 + \cdots + \alpha_k$$

be any vector of D, where α_i is in S_i. Since ϕ is in every S_i',

$$\alpha \cdot \phi = \alpha_1 \cdot \phi + \alpha_2 \cdot \phi + \cdots + \alpha_k \cdot \phi = 0.$$

Thus ϕ is in the orthogonal complement of D. Consequently M' is equal to the orthogonal complement of D.

Since S_i is the orthogonal complement of S_i', we apply the above result to the spaces S_1', S_2', $\cdots$, S_k'

and perceive that M is equal to the orthogonal complement of D'.

36. Divisors and multiples. As we have seen, every space of n-th order vectors can be spanned by the row vectors of an $n \times n$ matrix. If S_1 is spanned by fewer than n vectors, 0-vectors may be adjoined so as to bring this number up to n. Thus it will be no real restriction, and a great convenience, to assume that all matrices are square with n rows and columns. This will be assumed in the remainder of this chapter.

If three matrices A, C, D exist with elements in a field F such that

$$A = CD,$$

then D is called a *right divisor*, and C a *left divisor*, of A. Also A is called a *left multiple* of D and a *right multiple* of C.

If C is non-singular, it is both a left and a right divisor of every matrix A. For then C^{-1} exists, and we may define D and D_1 as the products

$$D = C^{-1}A, \qquad D_1 = AC^{-1}.$$

Thus $A = CD$ and $A = D_1C$.

But if C or D is singular, A is of the same or lower rank than either, so that A is clearly not arbitrary. If C is non-singular, A is called a *left associate* of D. Since $C^{-1}A = D$, D is also a left associate of A. If D is non-singular, A and C are *right associates*. If C is singular, A is a *proper left multiple* of D, and if D is singular, A is a *proper right multiple* of C.

If $A = O$, A is both a left and a right multiple of every matrix, for

$$O = O \cdot D = C \cdot O$$

for every C and D. But if A is not zero, C and D are each of the same or higher rank than A, so that they are not arbitrary. If $A = O$, C and D are divisors of zero (§26). If neither C nor D is O, they are both proper divisors of zero. As we have seen (Theorem 46), a matrix is a proper divisor of zero if and only if it is singular.

If D is a right divisor of two matrices A and B, and if D is a left multiple of every common right divisor of A and B, then D is called a *greatest common right divisor* (g.c.r.d.) of A and B. A common left multiple of two matrices A and B is called a *least common left multiple* (l.c.l.m.) of A and B if it is a right divisor of every common left multiple of A and B.

Similar definitions hold for *greatest common left divisor* and *least common right multiple*. Their properties are evidently similar to those of the g.c.r.d. and l.c.l.m.

If D is a greatest common right divisor of A and B, so is PD for every non-singular matrix P. For if

$$A = HD, \qquad B = KD,$$

then

$$A = HP^{-1}PD, \qquad B = KP^{-1}PD,$$

so that PD is a common right divisor of A and B. If D_1 is any common right divisor of A and B, then $D = LD_1$ by definition of g.c.r.d. Hence

$$PD = PLD_1,$$

so that D_1 is a right divisor of PD, which therefore is a greatest common right divisor of A and B.

Similarly if M is a least common left multiple of A and B, so is PM for every non-singular matrix P. For if

$$M = HA = KB,$$

then

$$PM = PHA = PKB$$

so that PM is a common left multiple of A and B. If M_1 is any common left multiple of A and B,

$$M_1 = LM = LP^{-1}PM,$$

so that PM is a least common left multiple of A and B.

We shall now prove

THEOREM 52. *Every pair of $n \times n$ matrices A and B have a greatest common right divisor D expressible in the form*

$$D = PA + QB.$$

Consider the matrix

$$G = \begin{bmatrix} A & O \\ B & O \end{bmatrix}$$

of order $2n$. By Theorem 18 there exists a non-singular matrix X of order $2n$ such that XG consists entirely of 0's except perhaps for the elements of the $n \times n$ block in the upper left corner. That is,

$$\begin{bmatrix} X_{11} & X_{12} \\ X_{21} & X_{22} \end{bmatrix} \begin{bmatrix} A & O \\ B & O \end{bmatrix} = \begin{bmatrix} D & O \\ O & O \end{bmatrix}$$

where the submatrices X_{ij} are obtained by cutting X up into $n \times n$ blocks. These blocks multiply like the elements of a matrix (see §10) so that

(28) $$X_{11}A + X_{12}B = D.$$

Now X is non-singular, so that it has an inverse Y which can likewise be cut into blocks. We have

$$\begin{bmatrix} A & O \\ B & O \end{bmatrix} = \begin{bmatrix} Y_{11} & Y_{12} \\ Y_{21} & Y_{22} \end{bmatrix} \begin{bmatrix} D & O \\ O & O \end{bmatrix}.$$

Thus

$$A = Y_{11}D, \qquad B = Y_{21}D.$$

These equations tell us that D is a common right divisor of A and B, and (28) shows that every common right divisor of A and B is a right divisor of D. Thus D is a g.c.r.d. of A and B.

The process is an extremely practicable one. Consider the matrices

$$A = \begin{bmatrix} 2 & 1 & 4 & 2 \\ -1 & 1 & 5 & 3 \\ 3 & 3 & 13 & 7 \\ 1 & 2 & 9 & 5 \end{bmatrix}, \quad B = \begin{bmatrix} -1 & 3 & 4 & 0 \\ 0 & -2 & 1 & 3 \\ 2 & 4 & 18 & 10 \\ 0 & 0 & 0 & 0 \end{bmatrix}.$$

We place these eight row vectors in one column and apply elementary transformations to them until as many as possible are made 0, and the rest are linearly independent. In the present example five can be made 0 and the remaining three can be taken to be

$$(-17, 1, 0, 0), \qquad (8, 1, 2, 0), \qquad (-3, 0, 1, 1).$$

Thus we have the g.c.r.d.

$$D = \begin{bmatrix} 0 & 0 & 0 & 0 \\ -17 & 1 & 0 & 0 \\ 8 & 1 & 2 & 0 \\ -3 & 0 & 1 & 1 \end{bmatrix}.$$

It should be noted that a g.c.r.d. in Hermite form (§12) can always be found.

37. Divisors and multiples of matric polynomials. If two matrices can be obtained from two polynomials $f_1(x)$ and $f_2(x)$ having scalar coefficients by substituting for x the same matrix A, a g.c.r.d. and a l.c.l.m. can be easily obtained.

Let $f_1(x)$ and $f_2(x)$ be two polynomials with coefficients in F, and let $d(x)$ be their greatest common divisor. Then there exist polynomials $h(x)$, $k(x)$, $p(x)$ and $q(x)$ with coefficients in F such that

$$f_1(x) = h(x) \cdot d(x), \qquad f_2(x) = k(x) \cdot d(x),$$
$$d(x) = p(x) \cdot f_1(x) + q(x) \cdot f_2(x).$$

Hence for every matrix A

$$f_1(A) = h(A) \cdot d(A), \qquad f_2(A) = k(A) \cdot d(A),$$
$$ⓣ \quad d(A) = p(A) \cdot f_1(A) + q(A) \cdot f_2(A).$$

Thus $d(A)$ is a g.c.r.d. of the matrices $f_1(A)$ and $f_2(A)$. — *since by ⓣ any matrix which divides $f_1(a) + f_2(a)$ divides $d(a)$*

Now let $m(x)$ be a least common multiple of the polynomials $f_1(x)$ and $f_2(x)$. There exist polynomials $h(x)$, $k(x)$, $p(x)$ and $q(x)$ with coefficients in F such that

$$m(x) = h(x) \cdot f_1(x) = k(x) \cdot f_2(x),$$
$$p(x) \cdot h(x) + q(x) \cdot k(x) = 1.$$

Then for every matrix A

$$m(A) = h(A) \cdot f_1(A) = k(A) \cdot f_2(A)$$

so that $m(A)$ is a common left multiple of $f_1(A)$ and $f_2(A)$.

That $m(A)$ is a least common left multiple of $f_1(A)$ and $f_2(A)$ is not so immediate. We must show that for every matrix M such that

$$Ⓚ \qquad M = H \cdot f_1(A) = K \cdot f_2(A)$$

there exists a matrix L such that $M = L \cdot m(A)$. It is not necessarily true that H, K, M or L is obtainable by substituting A for x in any polynomial. Now *(and therefore we do not necessarily have commutivity in ⊛)*

$$M \cdot h(A) = H \cdot f_1(A) \cdot h(A) = H \cdot m(A),$$
$$M \cdot k(A) = K \cdot f_2(A) \cdot k(A) = K \cdot m(A),$$
$$h(A) \cdot p(A) + k(A) \cdot q(A) = I.$$

Hence

$$M = M \cdot h(A) \cdot p(A) + M \cdot k(A) \cdot q(A)$$
$$= H \cdot m(A) \cdot p(A) + K \cdot m(A) \cdot q(A)$$
$$= (H \cdot p(A) + K \cdot q(A)) \cdot m(A).$$

Thus $m(A)$ is a right divisor of every common left multiple M, and we have proved

THEOREM 53. *If $d(x)$ is a greatest common divisor and $m(x)$ a least common multiple of the polynomials $f_1(x)$ and $f_2(x)$, then $d(A)$ is a g.c.r.d. and $m(A)$ is a l.c.l.m. of the matrices $f_1(A)$ and $f_2(A)$.*

38. Relation of the union to the greatest common right divisor. It will be the purpose of this section to prove

THEOREM 54. *Let A and B be $n \times n$ matrices whose row vectors span the respective linear spaces S_1 and S_2. Let D be a g.c.r.d., and let M be a l.c.l.m. of A and B. Then the row vectors of D span the union $S_1 \cup S_2$, and the row vectors of M span the intersection $S_1 \cap S_2$. Conversely every matrix whose row vectors span $S_1 \cup S_2$ is a g.c.r.d. of A and B, and every matrix whose row vectors span $S_1 \cap S_2$ is a l.c.l.m. of A and B.*

If D is a g.c.r.d. of A and B, there exist matrices H, K, P, Q such that

$$A = HD, \qquad B = KD, \qquad D = PA + QB.$$

Let the row vectors of D span the linear space S_3. Since $A = HD$, every row vector of A is a linear combination of the row vectors of D, so that $S_1 \subseteq S_3$. Similarly $S_2 \subseteq S_3$, so that $S_1 \cup S_2 \subseteq S_3$. Since $D = PA + QB$, every row vector of D is equal to the sum of a linear combination of row vectors of A and a linear combination of row vectors of B. Thus $S_3 \subseteq S_1 \cup S_2$, and accordingly D spans the linear space $S_1 \cup S_2$.

If M is a l.c.l.m. of A and B, there exist matrices H and K such that

$$M = HA = KB.$$

Let M span the space S_4. Since every row vector of M is a linear combination of row vectors of A, and also a linear combination of row vectors of B, $S_4 \subseteq S_1 \cap S_2$. Now let ϕ be any vector common to S_1 and S_2. There exist vectors κ and λ such that

$$\phi = \kappa \cdot A = \lambda \cdot B.$$

Let V, K, L denote the square matrices whose respective first rows are the components of ϕ, κ, λ, and the rest of whose elements are 0. Then

$$V = K \cdot A = L \cdot B$$

so that V is a common left multiple of A and B. Since M is a l.c.l.m., there exists a matrix H such that

$$V = H \cdot M.$$

Let η denote the first row vector of H. Then

$$\phi = \eta \cdot M.$$

That is, every vector which is common to S_1 and S_2 is equal to a linear combination of the row vectors of M. Hence $S_1 \cap S_2 \subseteq S_4$, and M spans $S_1 \cap S_2$.

Now let D_1 be any matrix which spans the union $\overline{S_1 \cup S_2.}$ By Theorem 25 there exists a non-singular matrix P such that $D_1 = PD$, so that D_1 is also a g.c.r.d. of A and B (§36). Similarly if M_1 is any matrix which spans the intersection $S_1 \cap S_2$, there exists a non-singular matrix Q such that $M_1 = QM$. Hence M_1 is also a l.c.l.m. of A and B.

[margin note: Then $r(D_1) = r(b)$ Since $r(D_1) = r(D) = r(S_1 \cup S_2)$]

Two properties of matrices are immediate from this theorem.

COROLLARY 54a. *If D is a g.c.r.d. and M a l.c.l.m. of A and B, then*

$$r(A) + r(B) = r(M) + r(D).$$

This follows immediately from Theorem 50.

COROLLARY 54b. *If D and D_1 are two greatest common right divisors of A and B, there exists a non-singular matrix P such that $D_1 = PD$. If M and M_1 are two least common left multiples of A and B, there exists a non-singular matrix Q such that $M_1 = QM$.*

These results follow from Theorem 25.

In §36 we had a practicable method for computing the g.c.r.d. of two matrices. With the aid of Theorem 51, this same method can be used to compute the l.c.l.m. From A and B we may compute their orthogonal complements A' and B' as in §34. Now we may find a g.c.r.d. D' of A' and B'. The orthogonal complement D of D' is a l.c.l.m. of A and B.

39. The sum of vector spaces. Let $m(x)$ be the minimum function of the $n \times n$ matrix A, and let

$$m(x) = m_1(x) \cdot m_2(x) \cdots m_k(x)$$

where the factors are relatively prime in pairs. In particular we may assume that each $m_i(x)$ is a power of an irreducible polynomial. The least common multiple of these factors is their product $m(x)$. Then, by Theorem 53, $m(A) = 0$ is a least common left multiple of the matrices

$$m_1(A), m_2(A), \cdots, m_k(A).$$

Let the row vectors of the matrices $m_i(A)$ span the respective linear spaces S_i, and let $[S_1, S_2, \cdots, S_k]$ denote their intersection. Since their l.c.l.m. is $m(A) = 0$, this intersection is 0, by Theorem 54. If S_i' is the orthogonal complement of S_i, we know by Theorem 51 that the union $(S_1', S_2', \cdots, S_k')$ is the orthogonal complement of $[S_1, S_2, \cdots, S_k]$, and is therefore of rank n. Thus the basic vectors of $S_1', S_2', \cdots, S_k'$ together span the total space S.

Since $m_1(x)$ is relatively prime to the product $m_2(x) \cdots m_k(x)$, the greatest common divisor of these two polynomials is 1. Then, by Theorem 53, I is a g.c.r.d. of the two matrices

$$m_1(A), \qquad m_2(A) \cdots m_k(A).$$

By Corollary 54a,

$$r(m_1(A)) + r(m_2(A) \cdots m_k(A)) = r(m(A)) + r(I) = n,$$

where r denotes rank. Similarly $m_2(x)$ is relatively prime to the product $m_3(x) \cdots m_k(x)$, so that a least common multiple of these two polynomials is their product, and

$$r(m_2(A)) + r(m_3(A) \cdots m_k(A)) = r(m_2(A) \cdots m_k(A)) + n.$$

We continue until we reach the $(k-1)$th equation

$$r(m_{k-1}(A)) + r(m_k(A)) = r(m_{k-1}(A) \cdot m_k(A)) + n.$$

Upon adding these $k-1$ equations, we have

$$r(m_1(A)) + r(m_2(A)) + \cdots + r(m_k(A)) = (k-1)n.$$

Now S_i' is the orthogonal complement of S_i, so that

$$r(S_i') = n - r(S_i) = n - r(m_i(A)).$$

Hence

$$r(S_1') + r(S_2') + \cdots + r(S_k') = kn - (k-1)n = n.$$

Denote $r(S_i')$ by r_i, and let

$$\sigma_{i1}, \sigma_{i2}, \cdots, \sigma_{ir_i}$$

be r_i vectors which span S_i'. The vectors

$$(29) \quad \sigma_{11}, \cdots, \sigma_{1r_1}, \sigma_{21}, \cdots, \sigma_{2r_2}, \cdots, \sigma_{k1}, \cdots, \sigma_{kr_k}$$

are n in number, since the sum of the ranks r_i is n. These n vectors are linearly independent, since they span S which is of rank n.

The union of subspaces is often called their *sum*. Thus S is the sum of the subspaces $S_1', S_2', \cdots, S_k'$ if the union $(S_1', S_2', \cdots, S_k')$ is of rank n. Then every vector ϕ of S is expressible in the form

$$\phi = \phi_1 + \phi_2 + \cdots + \phi_k$$

where ϕ_i is in S_i'. If every vector ϕ is uniquely expressible in this form, S is called the *supplementary sum* of the subspaces $S_1', S_2', \cdots, S_k'$. The uniqueness is equivalent to the linear independence of the basic vectors (29). For if

$$\phi = \phi_1 + \phi_2 + \cdots + \phi_k = \psi_1 + \psi_2 + \cdots + \psi_k$$

where ϕ_i and ψ_i are in S_i' and not every $\phi_i = \psi_i$, we should have

$$(\phi_1 - \psi_1) + (\phi_2 - \psi_2) + \cdots + (\phi_k - \psi_k) = 0.$$

This would yield a linear dependence relation among the basic vectors (29). Conversely, a dependence relation

for The ψ's can be written in Terms of the set (29) which span S

among the basic vectors would mean that 0 could be represented in two ways as a sum of vectors $\phi_1 + \phi_2 + \cdots + \phi_k$. } 1st way: the dependence relation } 2nd way: $0 \cdot \sigma_{11} + 0 \cdot \sigma_{12} + \cdots + 0 \cdot \sigma_{knk}$

We therefore have the important theorem,

THEOREM 55. *Let the minimum function $m(x)$ of the matrix A be written as a product of relatively prime factors $m_1(x) \cdot m_2(x) \cdots m_k(x)$. Let the row vectors of $m_i(A)$ span the space S_i and let S_i' be the orthogonal complement of S_i. Then the total space S is the supplementary sum of the subspaces $S_1', S_2', \cdots, S_k'$, and their basic vectors (29) together span S.*

The following example will illustrate this theorem. Let

$$A = \begin{bmatrix} -1 & 5 & 5 & 3 \\ 5 & 0 & -17 & -26 \\ -10 & -2 & 32 & 51 \\ 6 & 2 & -19 & -31 \end{bmatrix}.$$

If F is the rational field, the minimum function of A is

$$m(x) = m_1(x) \cdot m_2(x),$$

$$m_1(x) = x^2 + x + 1, \qquad m_2(x) = x^2 - x + 1,$$

$$m_1(A) = \begin{bmatrix} -6 & -4 & 18 & 32 \\ 14 & 8 & -42 & -72 \\ -24 & -14 & 72 & 124 \\ 14 & 8 & -42 & -72 \end{bmatrix},$$

$$m_2(A) = \begin{bmatrix} -4 & -14 & 8 & 26 \\ 4 & 8 & -8 & -20 \\ -4 & -10 & 8 & 22 \\ 2 & 4 & -4 & -10 \end{bmatrix}.$$

The row space S_1 of $m_1(A)$ is spanned by the vectors

$$(-1, 2, 3, 0), \qquad (0, -1, 0, 2)$$

and its orthogonal complement S_1' by the vectors

$$\sigma_{11} = (3, 0, 1, 0), \qquad \sigma_{12} = (0, 6, -4, 3).$$

The row space S_2 of $m_2(A)$ is spanned by the vectors

$$(-1, 3, 2, 0), \qquad (0, -1, 0, 1)$$

and its orthogonal complement S_2' by the vectors

$$\sigma_{21} = (2, 0, 1, 0), \qquad \sigma_{22} = (0, 2, -3, 2).$$

The matrix

$$\begin{bmatrix} \sigma_{11} \\ \sigma_{12} \\ \sigma_{21} \\ \sigma_{22} \end{bmatrix} = \begin{bmatrix} 3 & 0 & 1 & 0 \\ 0 & 6 & -4 & 3 \\ 2 & 0 & 1 & 0 \\ 0 & 2 & -3 & 2 \end{bmatrix}$$

is non-singular so that its row vectors span S.

40. Annihilators of vectors. Let A be an $n \times n$ matrix whose minimum function is

$$m(x) = m_1(x) \cdot m_2(x) \cdots m_k(x)$$

where the $m_i(x)$ are powers of distinct irreducible polynomials. That is,

$$m_1(x) = [l(x)]^h$$

where $l(x)$ is irreducible.

Since

$$[l(A)]^{i+1} = l(A) \cdot [l(A)]^i,$$

it is surely true that

$$r[l(A)]^i \geqq r[l(A)]^{i+1}$$

where r denotes rank. Suppose that for some i these ranks were equal. Denote by S_i the row space of $[l(A)]^i$ and by S_{i+1} the row space of $[l(A)]^{i+1}$. Every vector of S_{i+1} is in S_i so that $S_{i+1} \subseteq S_i$. If it were true that their ranks were the same, we should have $S_{i+1} = S_i$. Then by Theorem 25 there would exist a non-singular matrix M such that

$$[l(A)]^i = M \cdot [l(A)]^{i+1} \qquad i + 1 \leqq h.$$

Upon multiplying both sides on the right by

$$[l(A)]^{h-i-1} m_2(A) \cdots m_k(A),$$

we have

$$[l(A)]^{h-1} m_2(A) \cdots m_k(A) = M \cdot m(A) = 0,$$

contradicting the fact that $m(x)$ is the minimum function of A. Thus

$$(S_0) \supset S_1 \supset S_2 \supset \cdots \supset S_h.$$

If $B \cdot \phi = 0$, we shall call the matrix B an *annihilator* of the vector ϕ. All vectors annihilated by B constitute the *null space* of B. That is, the null space of B is the orthogonal complement of the row space of B. The dinension of the null space of B is called the *nullity* of B. It is equal to the order of B minus its rank.

Denote by S_i' the null space of $[l(A)]^i$. Since $r(S_i') = n - r(S_i)$, we have

$$S_0' \subset S_1' \subset S_2' \subset \cdots \subset S_h'.$$

We have proved

THEOREM 56. *If $[l(x)]^h$ is the highest power of the irreducible polynomial $l(x)$ which divides the minimum func-*

tion of A, and if S_i' is the null space of $[l(A)]^i$ for $1 \le i \le h$, there exists a vector which is in S_i' but not in S_{i-1}'.

Let $f(x)$ be any polynomial of degree $< ij$, and let $d(x)$ be the g.c.d. of $f(x)$ and $[l(x)]^i$. Then there exist polynomials $t(x)$ and $u(x)$ such that

$$t(x) \cdot f(x) + u(x) \cdot [l(x)]^i = d(x).$$

Let ϕ be a vector which is in the null space S_i' of $[l(A)]^i$ but not in the null space S_{i-1}' of $[l(A)]^{i-1}$. Then

$$t(A) \cdot f(A) \cdot \phi + u(A) \cdot [l(A)]^i \cdot \phi = d(A) \cdot \phi.$$

If $f(A) \cdot \phi = 0$, then $d(A) \cdot \phi = 0$; but $d(x)$ is of degree $< ij$, and is of the form $[l(x)]^h$, $h < i$, so that ϕ would be in S_{i-1}', contrary to its selection. Hence $f(A) \cdot \phi \ne 0$, and we have proved

COROLLARY 56. *If ϕ is a vector of the null space S_i' of $[l(A)]^i$ which is not in the null space S_{i-1}' of $[l(A)]^{i-1}$, then there exists no polynomial $f(x)$ of degree less than the degree of $[l(x)]^i$ such that $f(A) \cdot \phi = 0$.*

Let ϕ be in S_i' but not in S_{i-1}', and let

$$f(x) = c_0 + c_1 x + \cdots + c_{j-1} x^{j-1}$$

be any polynomial with coefficients in F of degree $\le j-1$ where j is the degree of $l(x)$. Then

$$[l(A)]^i \cdot f(A) \cdot \phi = f(A) \cdot [l(A)]^i \cdot \phi = 0$$

so that the vector $f(A) \cdot \phi$ is in S_i'. Since $f(x)$ is of lower degree than the degree of the irreducible polynomial $l(x)$, it is prime to $[l(x)]^i$. Hence there exist polynomials $t(x)$ and $u(x)$ such that

$$t(x) \cdot f(x) + u(x) \cdot [l(x)]^i = 1,$$
$$t(A) \cdot f(A) + u(A) \cdot [l(A)]^i = I,$$

and consequently

$$t(A) \cdot f(A) \cdot \phi = \phi.$$

If it were true that $f(A) \cdot \phi$ were in S'_{i-1}, we should have

$$[l(A)]^{i-1} \cdot f(A) \cdot \phi = 0,$$

and as a result,

$$t(A) \cdot [l(A)]^{i-1} \cdot f(A) \cdot \phi = [l(A)]^{i-1} \cdot \phi = 0$$

so that ϕ would be in S'_{i-1}, contrary to its selection. We have therefore proved all but the last statement of

THEOREM 57. *If $l(x)$, as defined in Theorem 56, is of degree j, and if ϕ is a vector of S'_i which is not in S'_{i-1}, the same is true of every vector of the form*

$$\circledast \quad c_0\phi + c_1 A\phi + c_2 A^2\phi + \cdots + c_{j-1} A^{i-1}\phi$$

the o vector is in every subspace

unless $c_0 = c_1 = \cdots = c_{j-1} = 0$. The vector $l(A) \cdot \phi$ is in S'_{i-1} but not in S'_{i-2}.

To prove the last statement, set

$$\psi = l(A) \cdot \phi.$$

If ϕ is in S'_i, then clearly

$$[l(A)]^{i-1} \cdot \psi = [l(A)]^i \cdot \phi = 0$$

so that ψ is in S'_{i-1}. If ψ were in S'_{i-2}, we should have

$$[l(A)]^{i-2} \cdot \psi = [l(A)]^{i-1} \cdot \phi = 0$$

so that ϕ would be in S'_{i-1}, contrary to its selection.

COROLLARY 57. *The null space S'_i of $[l(A)]^i$ is of dimension $d_i \geqq ij$ where j is the degree of $l(x)$. If A is non-derogatory with the minimum function $[l(A)]^h$, then $d_i = ij$.*

≤n rank ce ee of x) is n and o)^i | m(x)

By Theorem 57 the space S'_i contains at least j vectors

$$\psi, A\phi, A^2\phi, \cdots, A^{i-1}\phi$$

These can all be obtained from ⊛ by proper choice of the c's

Since any such lin. comb. can be written as ⑱ by a proper choice of the c's

which are in S_i' but not in S_{i-1}', and no linear combination $\neq 0$ of these vectors is in S_{i-1}'. Hence they are linearly independent, and the dimension d_i of S_i' is greater than the dimension d_{i-1} of S_{i-1}' by at least j. Moreover, S_1' is of dimension at least j so that

for if a lin. comb. with not all the c's o were o, then this lin. comb. would $\in S_{i-1}$, contradicting Th. 57

see bottom p. Top p.110 — every S_i' con at least j lin indep. vector.

$$d_i \geq d_{i-1} + j \geq d_{i-2} + 2j \geq \cdots$$
$$\geq d_1 + (i-1)j \geq j + (i-1)j = ij.$$

for the null space of $[l(A)]^{h_i}$ of ran n

If $n = hj$ and $[l(A)]^h = 0$, then $d_h = hj$, and for $i = h$ the first and last members of the above inequality are both hj. Thus every "$\geq$" must be an "$=$", so that $d_i = ij$.

We shall conclude with the following theorem.

THEOREM 58. *If $m(x)$ is the minimum function of a matrix A, there exists a vector which is in the null space of no matrix $m_0(A)$ where $m_0(x)$ is a proper divisor of $m(x)$.*

Let us set

see 1st sentence, p.111 ($m(x)$ itself as a divisor is excluded)

$$m_i(x) = [l_i(x)]^{h_i} \qquad (i = 1, 2, \cdots, k),$$

where the $l_i(x)$ are distinct irreducible polynomials. Let ϕ_i be a vector which is in the null space of $[l_i(A)]^{h_i}$ but not in the null space of any lower power of $l_i(A)$. By Theorem 56 such a vector exists. Define

$$\phi = \phi_1 + \phi_2 + \cdots + \phi_k.$$

Let $m_0(x)$ be any proper divisor of $m(x)$. Then

$$m_0(A) \cdot \phi = m_0(A) \cdot \phi_1 + m_0(A) \cdot \phi_2 + \cdots + m_0(A) \cdot \phi_k.$$

Since

$$m_i(A) \cdot m_0(A) \cdot \phi_i = m_0(A) \cdot m_i(A) \cdot \phi_i = 0,$$

and these null spaces $S_1', S_2', \cdots, S_k'$ are disj by Th 5:

$m_0(A) \cdot \phi_i$ is in the null space of $m_i(A)$. Then $m_0(A) \cdot \phi$ will be 0 if and only if $m_0(A) \cdot \phi_i = 0$ for every value of i, by Theorem 55.

on p.111 this is proved to be impossible.

If $m_0(x)$ is a proper divisor of $m(x)$, some one of the irreducible factors, say $l_i(x)$, occurs in $m_0(x)$ to a lower power than it occurs in $m(x)$. Let

$$m_0(x) = g(x) \cdot [l_i(x)]^f \qquad\qquad f < h_i$$

where $g(x)$ is relatively prime to $l_i(x)$. Then a greatest common divisor of $m_0(x)$ and $[l_i(x)]^{h_i}$ is $[l_i(x)]^f$, so that polynomials $t(x)$ and $u(x)$ exist such that

$$t(x) \cdot m_0(x) + u(x) \cdot [l_i(x)]^{h_i} = [l_i(x)]^f.$$

Hence

$$t(A) \cdot m_0(A) \cdot \phi_i = [l_i(A)]^f \cdot \phi_i.$$

If $m_0(A) \cdot \phi_i$ where 0, it would be true that $[l_i(A)]^f \cdot \phi_i$ =0, contrary to the selection of ϕ_i.

CHAPTER VI

THE RATIONAL CANONICAL FORM

41. Similar matrices. Two square matrices A and A' are called *similar* if there exists a non-singular matrix P such that

$$A' = P^{-1}AP.$$

We may use the notation $A' \overset{s}{=} A$ to denote similarity.

Since $A' = P^{-1}AP$ implies $A = PA'P^{-1}$, and therefore $A = (P^{-1})^{-1}A'(P^{-1})$, it is clear that $A' \overset{s}{=} A$ implies $A \overset{s}{=} A'$. Thus similarity is symmetric. Since $A = I^{-1}AI$, similarity is reflexive. Moreover, let

$$A' = P^{-1}AP, \qquad A'' = Q^{-1}A'Q$$

where both P and Q are, of course, non-singular. Then

$$A'' = Q^{-1}(P^{-1}AP)Q = (PQ)^{-1}A(PQ).$$

Hence $A' \overset{s}{=} A$ and $A'' \overset{s}{=} A'$ imply $A'' \overset{s}{=} A$ so that similarity is transitive. Thus similarity of matrices is a type of equals relation, or equivalence relation if you prefer. It is quite to be expected that such a relation will have important properties.

The concept of similarity is, in fact, one of the central ideas in matric theory. It appears in the study of groups of linear transformations, matric representations of algebras, pencils of quadratic forms, and in connection with various problems in projective geometry (see §56), and in other connections.

If

$$A' = P^{-1}AP, \qquad B' = P^{-1}BP,$$

then for every pair of numbers k and l of F,

$$kA' + lB' = P^{-1}(kA + lB)P, \qquad A'B' = P^{-1}(AB)P.$$

Since every polynomial in A is built from A by the operations of addition, multiplication and scalar multiplication, it follows that for every polynomial $f(x)$ with coefficients in F,

$$(30) \qquad P^{-1} \cdot f(A) \cdot P = f(A') = f(P^{-1} \cdot A \cdot P).$$

THEOREM 59. *Similar matrices have the same characteristic and minimum polynomials, the same determinant, norm and rank.*

Let $A' = P^{-1}AP$. Then

$$P^{-1}(xI - A)P = xI - P^{-1}AP = xI - A'$$

so that

$$d(xI - A') = d(P^{-1}) \cdot d(xI - A) \cdot d(P).$$

Since $d(P^{-1}) = 1/d(P)$, the characteristic polynomials are equal.

Let A and A' have the respective minimum polynomials $m(x)$ and $m'(x)$. Since

$$m(A') = P^{-1} \cdot m(A) \cdot P,$$

and since $m(A) = 0$, $m(A')$ is also 0. Then by Theorem 40, $m'(x)$ divides $m(x)$. Now $A = P \cdot A' \cdot P^{-1}$ so that the rôles of A and A' are interchangeable. Hence $m(x)$ likewise divides $m'(x)$ and, as each has 1 as its leading coefficient, they are equal.

Since the determinant of A is equal to the constant term of the characteristic function multiplied by $(-1)^n$ where n is the order of A, it is true that $d(A) = d(A')$. Similarly the norm of A is equal to the constant term of the minimum function multiplied by $(-1)^\mu$ where μ is the index of A, so that $n(A) = n(A')$. Since P and P^{-1} are non-singular, the ranks of A and A' are equal by Theorem 17.

42. The direct sum. Let A and B be two square matrices, A of order r and B of order s. The matrix

$$A \dotplus B = \begin{bmatrix} A & O \\ O & B \end{bmatrix}$$

of order $r+s$ is called their *direct sum*.

The following properties of the direct sum are elementary, and follow directly from the definition.

(a). $(A \dotplus B) \dotplus C = A \dotplus (B \dotplus C)$.

(b). $k(A \dotplus B) = kA \dotplus kB$ where k is in F.

(c). $(A_1 + A_2) \dotplus (B_1 + B_2) = (A_1 \dotplus B_1) + (A_2 \dotplus B_2)$.

(d). $(A_1 \dotplus B_1)(A_2 \dotplus B_2) = A_1 A_2 \dotplus B_1 B_2$.

(e). $(A \dotplus B)^T = A^T \dotplus B^T$.

(f). $(A \dotplus B)^{-1} = A^{-1} \dotplus B^{-1}$ if A and B are non-singular.

(g). $d(A \dotplus B) = d(A) \cdot d(B)$.

(h). $r(A \dotplus B) = r(A) + r(B)$.

(i). $A \dotplus B \overset{s}{=} B \dotplus A$.

It is understood that A_1 and A_2 are of the same order, and also that B_1 and B_2 are of the same order. It is not necessary that A_1 and B_1 be of the same order.

We shall derive two further properties, namely

(j). If $A' \overset{s}{=} A$ and $B' \overset{s}{=} B$, then $A' \dotplus B' \overset{s}{=} A \dotplus B$.

(k). If $f(x)$ is any polynomial,

$$f(A \dotplus B) = f(A) \dotplus f(B).$$

In order to prove (j), let

$$A' = P^{-1}AP, \qquad B' = Q^{-1}BQ.$$

Then by (d) and (f),

$$A' \dotplus B' = (P^{-1} \dotplus Q^{-1})(A \dotplus B)(P \dotplus Q)$$
$$= (P \dotplus Q)^{-1}(A \dotplus B)(P \dotplus Q).$$

To prove (k), let

$$f(x) = \sum_{i=0}^{n} c_i x^i.$$

By (d),

$$(A \dotplus B)^i = A^i \dotplus B^i$$

and by (b) and the last relation

$$c_i(A \dotplus B)^i = c_i A^i \dotplus c_i B^i.$$

The result now follows from (c).

More generally, let us suppose that the $n \times n$ matrix A of rank r can be written

$$A = A_1 \dotplus A_2 \dotplus \cdots \dotplus A_k = \begin{bmatrix} A_1 & O & \cdots & O \\ O & A_2 & \cdots & O \\ & \cdots \cdots \cdots & \\ O & O & \cdots & A_k \end{bmatrix}$$

where A_i is of order n_i and rank r_i. Let the row vectors of A span the space S, let the first n_1 row vectors of A span S_1, the next n_2 row vectors span S_2, etc. Denote by

$$\sigma_{i1}, \sigma_{i2}, \cdots, \sigma_{ir_i}$$

a set of basic vectors of S_i. By (h) the rank of S is $r_1 + r_2 + \cdots + r_k = r$. From the form of the matrix A it is clear that the vectors

$$\sigma_{11}, \cdots, \sigma_{1r_1}, \sigma_{21}, \cdots, \sigma_{2r_2}, \cdots, \sigma_{k1}, \cdots, \sigma_{kr_k}$$

are linearly independent (and span S, by def. of S). Thus S is the supplementary sum

$$S_1 + S_2 + \cdots + S_k$$

of the subspaces S_i. (See §39.)

It is moreover evident that, if ϕ_i is any vector of S_i, and if $i \neq j$,

$$\phi_i \cdot \phi_j = 0.$$

A supplementary sum of subspaces which has the additional property that every inner product of two vectors of different subspaces is 0 is called the *direct sum* of these subspaces, and we write

$$S = S_1 \dotplus S_2 + \cdots \dotplus S_k.$$

It is clear that if the matrix A is a direct sum of submatrices, its row space S is a direct sum of corresponding subspaces.

43. Invariant spaces. A subspace S_0 of S is said to be an *invariant space* of the matrix A if, for every vector ϕ of S_0, it is true that $A \cdot \phi$ is in S_0. If ϕ is any vector of an invariant space S_0 of A, then clearly $f(A) \cdot \phi$ is in S_0 for every polynomial $f(x)$.

In particular the null space of A is an invariant space of A, but A has invariant spaces other than its null space.

If S_1 and S_2 are invariant spaces of A, then clearly $S_1 \cup S_2$ and $S_1 \cap S_2$ are also invariant spaces of A.

THEOREM 60. *If A and B are commutative matrices, the null space of either is an invariant space of both.*

Let ϕ be any vector of the null space of A. Then $A \cdot \phi = 0$, and

$$AB \cdot \phi = BA \cdot \phi = 0$$

so that $B \cdot \phi$ is also in the null space of A. Thus the null space of A is an invariant space of B, for B. any vector in the null space of A is again in the null space of A.

COROLLARY 60. *If $f(x)$ and $g(x)$ are any two polynomials, the null space of $f(A)$ is an invariant space of $g(A)$.* (since $f(A)$ and $g(A)$ commute)

THEOREM 61. *If $f(A) \cdot \phi$ and $g(A) \cdot \phi$ are two vectors of the same invariant space S_0 of A, and if $d(x)$ is a greatest common divisor of $f(x)$ and $g(x)$, then $d(A) \cdot \phi$ is in S_0.*

It is not supposed that $\phi \in S_0$, for then we would have the theorem immediately by the 2nd sentence of §43.

The greatest common divisor $d(x)$ can be written in the form
$$d(x) = p(x) \cdot f(x) + q(x) \cdot g(x).$$
Then
$$d(A) \cdot \phi = p(A) \cdot f(A) \cdot \phi + q(A) \cdot g(A) \cdot \phi.$$
Since $f(A) \cdot \phi$ and $g(A) \cdot \phi$ are in S_0, so are $p(A) \cdot f(A) \cdot \phi$ and $q(A) \cdot g(A) \cdot \phi$, and so is their sum. since the sum of any two vectors of a vector space is again in the vector space

COROLLARY 61a. *If $f(A) \cdot \phi$ and $g(A) \cdot \phi$ are two vectors of the same invariant space S_0 of A, and if there exists no polynomial $h(x)$ of degree less than the degree of $f(x)$ such that $h(A) \cdot \phi$ is in S_0, then $f(x)$ divides $g(x)$.*

For unless $f(x)$ were a divisor of $g(x)$, they would have a greatest common divisor $d(x)$ of degree less than the degree of $f(x)$, whence by the theorem $d(A) \cdot \phi$ is in S_0.

COROLLARY 61b. *If $f(x)$ is a polynomial of lowest degree such that $f(A) \cdot \phi$ is in an invariant space S_0 of A, then $f(x)$ divides the minimum function $m(x)$ of A.*

Take $g(x) = m(x)$ in Corollary 61a. → $m(A) \cdot \phi \in S_0$ since $m(A) \cdot \phi = 0 \cdot \phi = 0$ and $0 \in$ any vector subspace.

Much of the importance of invariant spaces derives from the following result.

LEMMA 62. *Let the total vector space S be the supplementary sum of the subspaces*
$$S_1, S_2, \cdots, S_k$$

where each S_i is of dimension r_i and has the basis σ_{i1}, $\sigma_{i2}, \cdots, \sigma_{ir_i}$. Let P be the matrix whose column vectors are

(31) $\sigma_{11}, \cdots, \sigma_{1r_1}, \sigma_{21}, \cdots, \sigma_{2r_2}, \cdots, \sigma_{k1}, \cdots, \sigma_{kr_k}.$

If each space S_i is an invariant space of the matrix A, then

$$P^{-1}AP = B_1 \dotplus B_2 \dotplus \cdots \dotplus B_k$$

where B_i is a matrix of order r_i.

Since the vectors (31) span S (see §39), P is nonsingular. Now form the product

$$AP = [\beta_{11}, \cdots, \beta_{1r_1}, \beta_{21}, \cdots, \beta_{2r_2}, \cdots, \beta_{k1}, \cdots, \beta_{kr_k}]$$
$$= M,$$

the β's being the column vectors of M. Since each S_i is an invariant space of A, the vectors

$$\beta_{i1}, \beta_{i2}, \cdots, \beta_{ir_i}$$

are linear combinations of the vectors

$$\sigma_{i1}, \sigma_{i2}, \cdots, \sigma_{ir_i}$$

only, and do not involve the other σ's. Thus if $r_1 = 2$,

$$\beta_{11} = b_{111}\sigma_{11} + b_{112}\sigma_{12}, \qquad \beta_{12} = b_{121}\sigma_{11} + b_{122}\sigma_{12}$$

so that

$$[\beta_{11}, \beta_{12}] = [\sigma_{11}, \sigma_{12}] \begin{bmatrix} b_{111} & b_{121} \\ b_{112} & b_{122} \end{bmatrix}.$$

(handwritten annotations:)

since σ_{11} is in an invariant subspace of A

$AP = A[\sigma_{11}, \cdots, \sigma_{kr_k}] = [\beta_{11}, \cdots, \beta_{kr_k}]$

$A\sigma_{11} = \beta_{11} = b_{111}\sigma_{11} + b_{112}\sigma_{12} + \cdots + b_{1r_1}\sigma_{1r_1}$

$A\sigma_{12} = \beta_{12} = b_{121}\sigma_{11} + b_{122}\sigma_{12} + \cdots + b_{12r_1}\sigma_{1r_1}$

$A\sigma_{1r_1} = \beta_{1r_1} = b_{1r_11}\sigma_{11} + b_{1r_12}\sigma_{12} + \cdots + b_{1r_1r_1}\sigma_{1r_1}$

$[\beta_{11}, \beta_{12}, \cdots, \beta_{1r_1}] = [\sigma_{11}, \sigma_{12}, \cdots, \sigma_{1r_1}] \begin{bmatrix} b_{111} & b_{121} & \cdots & b_{1r_11} \\ b_{112} & b_{122} & \cdots & b_{1r_12} \\ b_{11r_1} & b_{12r_1} & \cdots & b_{1r_1r_1} \end{bmatrix}$

In general M can be written

$$\left[\sigma_{11}, \cdots, \sigma_{1r_1}, \sigma_{21}, \cdots, \sigma_{2r_2}, \cdots, \sigma_{k1}, \cdots, \sigma_{kr_k}\right] \begin{bmatrix} B_1 & O & \cdots & O \\ O & B_2 & \cdots & O \\ \cdot & \cdot & \cdot & \cdot \\ O & O & \cdots & B_k \end{bmatrix}$$

where each submatrix B_i has r_i rows and columns.

If we denote the last matrix by B, we have

$$AP = PB$$

or, since P is non-singular,

$$P^{-1}AP = B = B_1 \dotplus B_2 \dotplus \cdots \dotplus B_k.$$

We are now prepared to prove an important theorem in the theory of similarity.

THEOREM 62. *Let A be any $n \times n$ matrix with elements in a field F, and let*

$$m(x) = m_1(x) \cdot m_2(x) \cdots m_k(x)$$

be its minimum function expressed as a product of polynomials which are relatively prime in pairs. Let the null space of $m_i(A)$ be of rank r_i. Then A is similar to a direct sum

$$B_1 \dotplus B_2 \dotplus \cdots \dotplus B_k$$

where B_i is of order r_i, and the minimum function of B_i is $m_i(x)$.

If S_i' is the null space of $m_i(A)$, we know from Theorem 55 that the total space S is the supplementary sum of the subspaces

$$S_1', S_2', \cdots, S_k'.$$

By Corollary 60 each S_i' is an invariant subspace of A.

Then by Lemma 62 there exists a non-singular matrix P such that

$$P^{-1}AP = B_1 \dotplus B_2 \dotplus \cdots \dotplus B_k$$

where B_i is of order r_i.

Furthermore, by Corollary 60 each space S_j' is an invariant subspace of the matrix $m_i(A)$ for every i and j. Then by Lemma 62

$$\circledast \quad P^{-1} \cdot m_i(A) \cdot P = C_1 \dotplus C_2 \dotplus \cdots \dotplus C_k$$

where C_j is of order r_j, and the matrix P is the same as above. Since S_i' is the null space of $m_i(A)$, $m_i(A) \cdot \sigma_{ij} = 0$ so that C_i is a zero matrix of r_i rows and columns. But by (30) of §41,

$$P^{-1} \cdot m_i(A) \cdot P = m_i(P^{-1}AP)$$
$$= m_i(B_1 \dotplus B_2 \dotplus \cdots \dotplus B_k).$$

By (k) of §42 this is equal to

$$m_i(B_1) \dotplus m_i(B_2) \dotplus \cdots \dotplus m_i(B_k).$$

Consequently, $C_j = m_i(B_j)$, and in particular $m_i(B_i) = 0$. It then follows from Theorem 40 that $m_i(x)$ is divisible by the minimum function $m_i'(x)$ of B_i.

Since A and B are similar, they have the same minimum function $m(x)$ by Theorem 59. Define $m'(x)$ as the product

$$m'(x) = m_1'(x) \cdot m_2'(x) \cdots m_k'(x).$$

Then $m(x)$ is divisible by $m'(x)$. By Property (k) of §42,

$$m'(B) = m'(B_1) \dotplus m'(B_2) \dotplus \cdots \dotplus m'(B_k)$$
$$= m_1'(B_1) \cdot m_2'(B_1) \cdots m_k'(B_1)$$
$$\dotplus m_1'(B_2) \cdot m_2'(B_2) \cdots m_k'(B_2)$$
$$\dotplus \cdots \dotplus m_1'(B_k) \cdot m_2'(B_k) \cdots m_k'(B_k)$$

[handwritten: since $m_i'(x)$ is the min. polynom. of B_i]

Since $m_i'(B_i)=0$, it is true that $m'(B)=0$ so that $m'(x)$ is divisible by the minimum function $m(x)$ of B. Since $m(x)$ and $m'(x)$ each have leading coefficient 1, they are equal. Now if it were true that $m_i'(x)$ were a proper divisor of $m_i(x)$ for some value of i, it would follow that $m'(x)$ would be a proper divisor of $m(x)$, which is not true. Consequently for every value of i, $m_i(x)$ is the minimum function of B_i. *[handwritten: (since $m_i'(x)$ (see ⊗, p.121) is the min fn. of B_i]*

[handwritten margin right: $m'(x)|m(x)$ (⊕ p.120) and]

[handwritten margin left: ⊗ p.120 — (x) $m_i(x)$, every i]

We can illustrate this theorem by continuing with the example of §39. We have

$$A=\begin{bmatrix} -1 & 5 & 5 & 3 \\ 5 & 0 & -17 & -26 \\ -10 & -2 & 32 & 51 \\ 6 & 2 & -19 & -31 \end{bmatrix}, \quad P=\begin{bmatrix} 3 & 0 & 2 & 0 \\ 0 & 6 & 0 & 2 \\ 1 & -4 & 1 & -3 \\ 0 & 3 & 0 & 2 \end{bmatrix},$$

$$AP=A\left[\sigma_{11},\,\sigma_{12},\,\sigma_{21},\,\sigma_{22}\right]$$

$$=\left[\tfrac{2}{3}\sigma_{11}-\tfrac{1}{3}\sigma_{12},\,\tfrac{19}{3}\sigma_{11}-\tfrac{5}{3}\sigma_{12},\,\tfrac{3}{2}\sigma_{21}-\tfrac{7}{2}\sigma_{22},\,\tfrac{1}{2}\sigma_{21}-\tfrac{1}{2}\sigma_{22}\right]$$

$$=\left[\sigma_{11},\,\sigma_{12},\,\sigma_{21},\,\sigma_{22}\right]\begin{bmatrix} \tfrac{2}{3} & \tfrac{19}{3} & 0 & 0 \\ -\tfrac{1}{3} & -\tfrac{5}{3} & 0 & 0 \\ 0 & 0 & \tfrac{3}{2} & \tfrac{1}{2} \\ 0 & 0 & -\tfrac{7}{2} & -\tfrac{1}{2} \end{bmatrix}=PB.$$

The minimum functions of the matrices

$$B_1=\begin{bmatrix} \tfrac{2}{3} & \tfrac{19}{3} \\ -\tfrac{1}{3} & -\tfrac{5}{3} \end{bmatrix}, \quad B_2=\begin{bmatrix} \tfrac{3}{2} & \tfrac{1}{2} \\ -\tfrac{7}{2} & -\tfrac{1}{2} \end{bmatrix}$$

are, respectively,

$$m_1(x)=x^2+x+1, \quad m_2(x)=x^2-x+1.$$

44. The non-derogatory case. Let the matrix A be non-derogatory of order and index n, and let its minimum function be

$$m(x) = m_0 + m_1 x + \cdots + m_{n-1} x^{n-1} + x^n.$$

Let ϕ be a vector which is not annihilated by any matrix $m_0(A)$ where $m_0(x)$ is a proper divisor of $m(x)$. By Theorem 58 such a vector exists. Consider the n vectors

$$(32) \qquad \phi, A\phi, A^2\phi, \cdots, A^{n-1}\phi.$$

If these vectors were linearly dependent, there would exist a relation

$$c_0\phi + c_1 A\phi + c_2 A^2\phi + \cdots + c_{n-1} A^{n-1}\phi = 0$$

which could be written

$$f(A) \cdot \phi = 0, \qquad f(x) = c_0 + c_1 x + \cdots + c_{n-1} x^{n-1} \neq 0.$$

Let $d(x)$ be the greatest common divisor of $f(x)$ and $m(x)$. Since $f(x)$ is of degree $< n$, $d(x) \neq m(x)$. Then there exist polynomials $p(x)$ and $q(x)$ such that

$$p(x) \cdot f(x) + q(x) \cdot m(x) = d(x)$$

and consequently

$$p(A) \cdot f(A) \cdot \phi + q(A) \cdot m(A) \cdot \phi = d(A) \cdot \phi$$

so that $d(A) \cdot \phi = 0$. But $d(x)$ is a proper divisor of $m(x)$ so that ϕ cannot be annihilated by $d(A)$. Hence the vectors (32) are linearly independent.

Denote by P the matrix whose column vectors are given by (32). Since these$_{\wedge}^{(n)}$ vectors are linearly independent, P is non-singular. Now form the product

$$AP = A\left[\phi, A\phi, A^2\phi, \cdots, A^{n-1}\phi\right]$$

$$= \left[A\phi, A^2\phi, \cdots, -m_0\phi - m_1A\phi - \cdots - m_{n-1}A^{n-1}\phi\right]$$

$$= \left[\phi, A\phi, A^2\phi, \cdots, A^{n-1}\phi\right]
\begin{bmatrix}
0 & 0 & \cdots & 0 & -m_0 \\
1 & 0 & \cdots & 0 & -m_1 \\
0 & 1 & \cdots & 0 & -m_2 \\
\cdot & \cdot & \cdot & \cdot & \cdot \\
0 & 0 & \cdots & 1 & -m_{n-1}
\end{bmatrix} = PC.$$

Thus $P^{-1}AP = C$ where C is the companion matrix (§31) of the minimum equation of A, and we have proved

THEOREM 63. *Every non-derogatory matrix is similar to the companion matrix of its minimum equation.*

Now suppose that we write

$$m(x) = m_1(x) \cdot m_2(x) \cdots m_k(x)$$

where the $m_i(x)$ are relatively prime in pairs, and the sum of their degrees is n. By Theorem 62 we know that there exists a non-singular matrix P such that

$$P^{-1}AP = B_1 \dotplus B_2 \dotplus \cdots \dotplus B_k = B$$

where $m_i(x)$ is the minimum function of B_i. (We know that the degree of the minimum function is less than or equal to the order of the matrix,) and that the sum of the orders of the B_i is n. If for some i the degree of $m_i(x)$ were less than the order of B_i, the degree of $m(x)$ would be less than n, which is not true. Hence every B_i is non-derogatory.

By Theorem 63 there exists a non-singular matrix Q_i such that

$$Q_i^{-1} B_i Q_i = C_i$$

where C_i is the companion matrix of the equation $m_i(x) = 0$. Then as in the proof of Property (k) of §42,

$$Q^{-1} B Q = C_1 \dotplus C_2 \dotplus \cdots \dotplus C_k,$$

where

$$Q = Q_1 \dotplus Q_2 \dotplus \cdots \dotplus Q_k.$$

Consequently

$$Q^{-1} P^{-1} A P Q = C_1 \dotplus C_2 \dotplus \cdots \dotplus C_k$$

and we have

THEOREM 64. *If the matrix A is non-derogatory, and if its minimum function is*

$$m(x) = m_1(x) \cdot m_2(x) \cdots m_k(x)$$

where the factors are relatively prime in pairs, then A is similar to the direct sum of the companion matrices of the factors $m_i(x)$.

Let us return to the example used in §43. Let us choose $\phi = (1, 0, 0, 0)$. Then

$$P = [\phi, A\phi, A^2\phi, A^3\phi] = \begin{bmatrix} 1 & -1 & -6 & 5 \\ 0 & 5 & 9 & 0 \\ 0 & -10 & -14 & 2 \\ 0 & 6 & 8 & 0 \end{bmatrix},$$

$$P^{-1} = \begin{bmatrix} 1 & \frac{9}{7} & -\frac{5}{2} & -\frac{71}{14} \\ 0 & -\frac{4}{7} & 0 & \frac{9}{14} \\ 0 & \frac{3}{7} & 0 & -\frac{5}{14} \\ 0 & \frac{1}{7} & \frac{1}{2} & \frac{5}{7} \end{bmatrix}.$$

We find that

$$P^{-1}AP = \begin{bmatrix} 0 & 0 & 0 & -1 \\ 1 & 0 & 0 & 0 \\ 0 & 1 & 0 & -1 \\ 0 & 0 & 1 & 0 \end{bmatrix},$$

which is the companion matrix of the minimum equation

$$m(x) = x^4 + x^2 + 1 = 0.$$

The second canonical form can be obtained from the matrices B_1 and B_2 of §43. Let

$$Q_1 = \begin{bmatrix} 1 & \frac{2}{3} \\ 0 & -\frac{1}{3} \end{bmatrix}, \qquad Q_2 = \begin{bmatrix} 1 & \frac{3}{2} \\ 0 & -\frac{7}{2} \end{bmatrix}.$$

Then

$$Q_1^{-1}B_1Q_1 = \begin{bmatrix} 0 & -1 \\ 1 & -1 \end{bmatrix}, \qquad Q_2^{-1}B_2Q_2 = \begin{bmatrix} 0 & -1 \\ 1 & 1 \end{bmatrix}$$

are the companion matrices of the equations obtained from the respective factors x^2+x+1 and x^2-x+1 of the minimum function of A. Then A is similar to the matrix

$$\begin{bmatrix} 0 & -1 & 0 & 0 \\ 1 & -1 & 0 & 0 \\ 0 & 0 & 0 & -1 \\ 0 & 0 & 1 & 1 \end{bmatrix}.$$

45. A canonical form. As we saw in Theorem 62, every matrix with elements in F is similar to a direct sum of matrices whose minimum functions are powers of irreducible polynomials. We shall restrict attention, then, to an $n \times n$ matrix A of index μ whose minimum function is

$$m(x) = [l(x)]^h \qquad\qquad \mu = jh,$$

$$l(x) = l_0 + l_1 x + l_2 x^2 + \cdots + l_{j-1} x^{j-1} + x^j.$$

Let ϕ be a vector which is in the null space of $[l(A)]^h$ and not in the null space of $[l(A)]^{h-1}$. Such a vector exists by Theorem 56. Denote $[l(A)]^i \cdot \phi$ by ϕ_i, and form the set of vectors

(33)
$$\phi, A\phi, A^2\phi, \cdots, A^{i-1}\phi, \phi_1, A\phi_1, A^2\phi_1, \cdots, A^{i-1}\phi_1,$$
$$\cdots, \phi_{h-1}, A\phi_{h-1}, A^2\phi_{h-1}, \cdots, A^{i-1}\phi_{h-1}.$$

These vectors are $jh = \mu$ in number, and we shall prove that they are linearly independent. If there were a linear relation among these vectors, it would take the form

$$f(A) \cdot \phi = 0, \qquad f(x) = c_0 + c_1 x + c_2 x^2 + \cdots + c_{\mu-1} x^{\mu-1}.$$

But by Corollary 56 this is impossible.

It may be well to note at this point that the vectors

(34)
$$\phi, A\phi, A^2\phi, \cdots, A^{\mu-1}\phi$$

are also linearly independent, and span the same space as is spanned by the vectors (33).

Let us now consider the non-derogatory case in which $\mu = n$. The vectors (33) are now n in number and linearly independent so that they span S. Let P be the matrix whose column vectors are the vectors (33). Form the product AP.

To relieve the notation, let us assume

$$h = 3, \qquad j = 3, \qquad l(x) = l_0 + l_1 x + l_2 x^2 + x^3.$$

Then

$$A^3\phi = l(A)\cdot\phi - l_0\phi - l_1A\phi - l_2A^2\phi,$$
$$A^3\phi_1 = l(A)\cdot\phi_1 - l_0\phi_1 - l_1A\phi_1 - l_2A^2\phi_1,$$
$$A^3\phi_2 = \qquad - l_0\phi_2 - l_1A\phi_2 - l_2A^2\phi_2.$$

$$AP = [A\phi, A^2\phi, - l_0\phi - l_1A\phi - l_2A^2\phi + \phi_1,$$
$$A\phi_1, A^2\phi_1, - l_0\phi_1 - l_1A\phi_1 - l_2A^2\phi_1 + \phi_2,$$
$$A\phi_2, A^2\phi_2, - l_0\phi_2 - l_1A\phi_2 - l_2A^2\phi_2]$$

$$= [\phi, A\phi, A^2\phi, \phi_1, A\phi_1, A^2\phi_1, \phi_2, A\phi_2, A^2\phi_2]B = PB$$

(handwritten margin note):
$$l(A)\cdot\phi_2 = 0$$
since
$$l(A)\cdot\phi_2 =$$
$$l(A)\cdot[l(A)]^2\phi$$
$$[l(A)]^3\cdot\phi$$
$$[l(A)]^2\cdot\phi$$

where

$$(35)\quad B = \begin{bmatrix} 0 & 0 & -l_0 & 0 & 0 & 0 & 0 & 0 & 0 \\ 1 & 0 & -l_1 & 0 & 0 & 0 & 0 & 0 & 0 \\ 0 & 1 & -l_2 & 0 & 0 & 0 & 0 & 0 & 0 \\ 0 & 0 & 1 & 0 & 0 & -l_0 & 0 & 0 & 0 \\ 0 & 0 & 0 & 1 & 0 & -l_1 & 0 & 0 & 0 \\ 0 & 0 & 0 & 0 & 1 & -l_2 & 0 & 0 & 0 \\ 0 & 0 & 0 & 0 & 0 & 1 & 0 & 0 & -l_0 \\ 0 & 0 & 0 & 0 & 0 & 0 & 1 & 0 & -l_1 \\ 0 & 0 & 0 & 0 & 0 & 0 & 0 & 1 & -l_2 \end{bmatrix}.$$

(handwritten note): see (9) p. 114

It is clear that

$$d(xI - B) = \begin{vmatrix} x & 0 & l_0 \\ -1 & x & l_1 \\ 0 & -1 & x + l_2 \end{vmatrix}^3.$$

As we saw in §31, the displayed determinant is the characteristic determinant of the companion matrix of $l(x) = 0$, so that

$$d(xI - B) = [l(x)]^3.$$

see middle, p. 82

Now $xI - B$ has an $(n-1)$-rowed minor determinant in the lower left-hand corner which is equal to ± 1, so that by Theorem 41 the minimum function of B is $[l(x)]^3$. *(expand on minors of 1st column, and so*

In general the matrix of type (35) whose minimum function is $[l(x)]^h$ will have along the principal diagonal h blocks, each of which is the companion matrix of $l(x) = 0$. The diagonal just below the principal diagonal consists entirely of 1's. We have

THEOREM 65. *Every non-derogatory matrix whose minimum function is $[l(x)]^h$ where $l(x)$ is irreducible of degree j is similar to a matrix of the type (35) with h blocks along the diagonal.*

The case where F is the complex field, or in fact any algebraically closed field, deserves special mention. In this case we can write

$$m(x) = (x - x_1)^{h_1}(x - x_2)^{h_2} \cdots (x - x_k)^{h_k}$$

so that A is similar to a direct sum of matrices of the form

$$(36) \qquad B_i = \begin{bmatrix} x_i & 0 & 0 & \cdots & 0 & 0 \\ 1 & x_i & 0 & \cdots & 0 & 0 \\ 0 & 1 & x_i & \cdots & 0 & 0 \\ 0 & 0 & 1 & \cdots & 0 & 0 \\ \cdot & \cdot & \cdot & \cdot & \cdot & \cdot \\ 0 & 0 & 0 & \cdots & 1 & x_i \end{bmatrix},$$

of h_i rows and columns. This is the familiar *Jordan normal form* of a matrix with complex elements.

46. The derogatory case. If A has the minimum function

$$m(x) = [l(x)]^h \qquad\qquad jh = \mu < n,$$

invariant since A . any vector in it is a lin.
comb. of powers of A·φ, the biggest being
perhaps A^u·φ which again ∈ Σ₁ —see
expressio
for A³φ₂
P. 127,
Top

the vectors (33) will span an invariant subspace Σ_1 of S, but will not span S. There will exist, then, vectors which are linearly independent of the vectors (33). For each such vector ψ',

$$[l(A)]^h \cdot \psi' = 0 \qquad = m(A) \cdot \psi' = 0 \cdot \psi'$$

which is surely in Σ_1, while

$$[l(A)]^0 \cdot \psi' = I \cdot \psi' = \psi'$$

is not in Σ_1. For each such vector ψ', therefore, there exists an integer k, $0 < k \leq h$, such that $[l(A)]^k \cdot \psi'$ is in Σ_1 while $[l(A)]^{k-1} \cdot \psi'$ is not in Σ_1.

Of all such vectors ψ', choose one whose corresponding integer k is maximal, and call it ψ''. There will exist a relation

$$[l(A)]^k \cdot \psi'' = g(A) \cdot \phi \qquad 1 \leq k \leq h.$$

since
[l(A)]^k·ψ'
∈ Σ₁

By the division algorithm we can determine polynomials $q(x)$ and $r(x)$, the latter either zero or of degree less than jk, such that

$$g(x) = [l(x)]^k \cdot q(x) + r(x).$$

Then

$$[l(A)]^k \cdot \psi'' = [l(A)]^k \cdot q(A) \cdot \phi + r(A) \cdot \phi.$$

Multiplying on the left by $[l(A)]^{h-k}$, we have

$$m(A) \cdot \psi'' = m(A) \cdot q(A) \cdot \phi + [l(A)]^{h-k} \cdot r(A) \cdot \phi$$

so that

$$[l(A)]^{h-k} \cdot r(A) \cdot \phi = 0.$$

The polynomial

$$[l(x)]^{h-k} \cdot r(x)$$

is 0 or of degree less than $j(h-k)+jk=\mu$, which is impossible by Corollary 56. Hence the polynomial is iden-

Suppose a polynomial g(x) is a polynomial of lowest degree ∋ g(A)·φ...
Since Σ₁ is an invariant subspace, by cor. 61 & g(x)|m(x). Thus g(x) is
of the form [l(A)]ʲ a≤j≤h. Clearly j≠h, for [l(A)]could not then
of lowest degree since [l(A)]ʰ ψ=0 ∈Σ₁ and we would have h<

tically zero, and $r(x) = 0$. Then there exists a relation of
the form

$$\odot \quad [l(A)]^k \cdot \psi'' = [l(A)]^k \cdot q(A) \cdot \phi \qquad 1 \leq k \leq h.$$

We shall now define a new vector

$$\psi = \psi'' - q(A) \cdot \phi.$$

It is clear that

$$\odot \quad [l(A)]^k \cdot \psi = 0,$$

which is in Σ_1. Consider the equation

$$[l(A)]^{k-1} \cdot \psi = [l(A)]^{k-1} \cdot \psi'' - [l(A)]^{k-1} \cdot q(A) \cdot \phi.$$

Since Σ_1 is an invariant subspace, the last term is in Σ_1.
If the left member were also in Σ_1, then

$$[l(A)]^{k-1} \cdot \psi''$$

would be in Σ_1, contrary to the definition of k. Thus ψ is
a vector whose corresponding integer k is maximal, and
by Corollary 61b, $[l(x)]^k$ is a polynomial $p(x)$ of smallest
degree such that $p(A) \cdot \psi$ is in Σ_1. $\otimes$

We shall now prove that the vectors

$$(37) \quad \begin{array}{l} \psi, A\psi, A^2\psi, \cdots, A^{j-1}\psi, \psi_1, A\psi_1, A^2\psi_1, \cdots, A^{j-1}\psi_1, \\ \cdots, \psi_{k-1}, A\psi_{k-1}, A^2\psi_{k-1}, \cdots, A^{j-1}\psi_{k-1} \end{array}$$

where $\psi_i = [l(A)]^i \cdot \psi$ are linearly independent and form
with the vectors (33) a linearly independent set, and
span an invariant subspace Σ_2 of S.

If the vectors (37) were linearly dependent among
themselves, or if they were linearly dependent upon the
vectors (33), there would exist a relation

$$f(A) \cdot \psi = g(A) \cdot \phi$$

with $f(x)$ of degree $< jk$ and $g(x)$ either 0 or of degree
$< jh$. By Corollary 61a, $f(x)$ is divisible by $[l(x)]^k$, which

which is impossible by ⊕

is of degree jk. Hence $f(x) = 0$ and no linear relation among the vectors (33) and (37) can exist.   ✳

Since $A \cdot \psi$ = lin. comb. of lower powers of A · ψ

Since $[l(A)]^k \cdot \psi = 0$, the product by A of each vector of (37) is equal to a linear combination of these vectors. Thus the space Σ_2 spanned by the vectors (37) is invariant under A and is of rank (or dimension) jk. *since there are jk independent vectors in (37)*

47. Continuation of the derogatory case.
We shall carry the process one step further. This third step is characteristic of the general case.

Either $\Sigma_1 \cup \Sigma_2 = S$, or else there exist vectors χ' which are not in $\Sigma_1 \cup \Sigma_2$. For each such vector χ' there exists an integer e such that $[l(A)]^e \cdot \chi'$ is in the union, while $[l(A)]^{e-1} \cdot \chi'$ is not in the union. Let χ'' be one such vector whose corresponding integer e is maximal. Since in the previous step ψ was chosen with a maximal k, it will be true that $0 < e \leqq k \leqq h$.

since $[l(A)]^e \cdot \chi' = 0$ belongs to the union, while $[l(A)]^0 \cdot \chi' = I \cdot \chi' = \chi' \notin$ the union

Suppose $e > k$. Then since $[l(A)]^{e-1} \cdot \chi'' \notin \Sigma_1 \cup \Sigma_2$, it $\notin \Sigma_1$.

There will exist a relation *Hence χ'' will furnish a maximal k for some k ∴ contradict. the supposition.*

$$[l(A)]^e \cdot \chi'' = g_1(A) \cdot \phi + g_2(A) \cdot \psi.$$

We can write *for any vector in the union is a lin. comb. of (37) and (33)*

$$g_1(x) = [l(x)]^e \cdot q_1(x) + r_1(x),$$
$$g_2(x) = [l(x)]^e \cdot q_2(x) + r_2(x)$$

where each of $r_1(x)$ and $r_2(x)$ is 0 or of degree $< je$. Then

⑤ $[l(A)]^k \cdot \chi'' = [l(A)]^{k-e}[g_1(A) \cdot \phi + g_2(A) \cdot \psi],$

if not in Σ_1 then χ'' will furnish a k greater than the maximal k

$[l(A)]^k \cdot \chi'' - [l(A)]^{k-e} \cdot g_1(A) \cdot \phi - \underline{[l(A)]^k \cdot q_2(A) \cdot \psi}$ *=0* *see ⑨ p.130*

$$= [l(A)]^{k-e} \cdot r_2(A) \cdot \psi.$$

By the definition of k, and the fact that ϕ is in Σ_1, the entire left member of the above equation is in Σ_1, while the right member is in Σ_2. But $\Sigma_1 \cap \Sigma_2 = 0$ so that each *by ⑦ above* member is 0. Then by Corollary 61a, $[l(x)]^{k-e} \cdot r_2(x)$ is divisible by $[l(x)]^k$, whence $r_2(x) = 0$.

have t show at ∴ $r_2(A) \cdot \psi = 0$ and hence $\varepsilon \Sigma_1$. ⓧ, p.130, $]^k$ is polynom. smallest degree $[l(x)]^k \cdot \psi \varepsilon \Sigma_1$

either $r_2(x)$ is 0 or Since $[l(x)]^{k-e} r_2(x)$ is of degree less than $j(k-e)+je = jk$, contradicting fact that $[l(x)]^k | [l(x)]^{k-e} r_2(x)$

[handwritten top marginalia:] Consider the invariant space of A, S_A, consisting only of the zero vector. Then $[\ell(A)]^{h-e} \cdot R_1(A) \cdot \phi = 0 \in S_A$, $[\ell(A)]^h \cdot \phi = [m(A)] \cdot \phi = 0 \in S_A$ By Cor. 56 ∃ no polynom. $\ell(x)$ of degree $< j\ell$ (by the choice of ϕ) ∋ $\ell(A) \cdot$ — Then by Cor. 61a we have the required divisibility

We now have *[handwritten:]* multiplying thru in ⓢ p.131 by $[\ell(A)]^{h-\ell}$

$$m(A) \cdot \chi'' = [l(A)]^{h-e}[g_1(A) \cdot \phi + g_2(A) \cdot \psi],$$
$$= m(A) \cdot q_1(A) \cdot \phi + [l(A)]^{h-e} \cdot r_1(A) \cdot \phi$$
$$+ m(A) \cdot q_2(A) \cdot \psi. \quad \text{(note } R_2(x)=0; \text{ see bottom, last page)}$$

[handwritten brace, left:] { That is, $[l(A)]^{h-e} \cdot r_1(A) \cdot \phi = 0$. Hence $[l(x)]^{h-e} \cdot r_1(x)$ is divisible by $[l(x)]^h$, and consequently $r_1(x) = 0$.

We define χ by the equation

$$\chi = \chi'' - q_1(A) \cdot \phi - q_2(A) \cdot \psi.$$

Then clearly

$$[l(A)]^e \cdot \chi = 0.$$

If $[l(A)]^{e-1} \cdot \chi$ were in $\Sigma_1 \cup \Sigma_2$, we should have

$$[l(A)]^{e-1} \cdot \chi'' = \boxed{[l(A)]^{e-1} \cdot q_1(A) \cdot \phi} + \boxed{[l(A)]^{e-1} \cdot q_2(A) \cdot \psi} \in \Sigma_2$$
$$+ [l(A)]^{e-1} \cdot \chi \quad = q_1(A) \cdot [\ell(A)]^{e-1} \cdot \phi \quad \text{(see)}$$
$$\in \text{invariant space } \Sigma_1 \text{ of}$$

which would be in $\Sigma_1 \cup \Sigma_2$, contrary to the definition of χ''. Thus χ is a vector whose corresponding integer e is *[handwritten left margin:]* $\chi \notin \Sigma_1 \cup \Sigma_2$, { For if it did $\chi'' = \chi + q_1(A) \cdot \phi + q_2(A) \psi$ would $\in \Sigma_1 \cup \Sigma_2$. maximal, and such that

$$[l(A)]^e \cdot \chi = 0, \qquad [l(A)]^{e-1} \cdot \chi \text{ not in } \Sigma_1 \cup \Sigma_2.$$

[handwritten left margin:] e is then maximal by the original choice of χ'' We now consider the subspace Σ_3 spanned by the vectors

$$(38) \quad \chi, A\chi, A^2\chi, \cdots, A^{i-1}\chi, \chi_1, A\chi_1, A^2\chi_1, \cdots, A^{j-1}\chi_1,$$
$$\cdots, \chi_{e-1}, A\chi_{e-1}, A^2\chi_{e-1}, \cdots, A^{j-1}\chi_{e-1}$$

where $\chi_i = [l(A)]^i \cdot \chi$. As before we prove that these vectors are linearly independent among themselves.

Suppose that there were a linear relation among the vectors (33), (37) and (38). It would take the form

$$f(A) \cdot \chi = g_1(A) \cdot \phi + g_2(A) \cdot \psi$$

where $f(x)$ is 0 or of degree $< je$, $g_1(x)$ is 0 or of degree

$< jh$ and $g_2(x)$ is 0 or of degree $< jk$. If $f(x) \neq 0$, we may write

$$f(x) = f_1(x) \cdot [l(x)]^i \qquad 0 \leqq i < e$$

where $f_1(x)$ is relatively prime to $l(x)$ and hence to $m(x)$, so that $f_1(A)$ has the inverse $f_1^{-1}(A)$. Then

$$[l(A)]^i \cdot \chi = f_1^{-1}(A) \cdot g_1(A) \cdot \phi + f_1^{-1}(A) \cdot g_2(A) \cdot \psi$$

where $i < e$. But for $i < e$ the vector $[l(A)]^i \cdot \chi$ cannot be in the union $\Sigma_1 \cup \Sigma_2$. Hence the vectors (33), (37) and (38) are linearly independent.

Since $[l(A)]^e \cdot \chi = 0$, the space Σ_3 is invariant under A.

As long as there remains a vector which is not in the union of the invariant spaces

$$\Sigma_1, \Sigma_2, \Sigma_3, \cdots$$

we can find another invariant space whose basic vectors are of the same form as (33), and are linearly independent of the basic vectors of the union of the spaces previously obtained. In a finite number of steps we obtain the total space S expressed as a supplementary sum of such subspaces,

$$S = \Sigma_1 + \Sigma_2 + \cdots + \Sigma_t.$$

We have proved

THEOREM 66. *If the matrix A has the minimum function $[l(x)]^{h_1}$ where $l(x)$ is irreducible, the total vector space S can be written as a sum of subspaces*

$$S = \Sigma_1 + \Sigma_2 + \cdots + \Sigma_t$$

each of which is an invariant space of A, and each of which has a basis of the form (33) with $h \leqq h_1$.

48. The rational canonical form. If $S = \Sigma_1 + \Sigma_2 + \cdots$

$+\Sigma_t$ is any decomposition of S into subspaces each of which is an invariant space of A, and if

$$\sigma_{i1}, \sigma_{i2}, \cdots, \sigma_{ir_i}$$

is any basis for Σ_i, we may form the matrix P whose column-vectors are

$$\sigma_{11}, \cdots, \sigma_{1r_1}, \sigma_{21}, \cdots, \sigma_{2r_2}, \cdots, \sigma_{t1}, \cdots, \sigma_{tr_i}.$$

By Lemma 62

$$P^{-1}AP = B_1 + B_2 + \cdots + B_t$$

where B_i is of order r_i. Then by (k) of §42

$$m(A) = m(P^{-1}AP) = m(B_1) + m(B_2) + \cdots + m(B_t)$$

so that

$$m(B_i) = 0,$$

and the minimum function of B_i is a divisor of the minimum function $[l(x)]^h$ of A. But it may not be true that each B_i is non-derogatory.

If, however, we assume the particular decomposition of S described in Theorem 66, and if we take (33) as the basis for Σ_1, (37) as the basis for Σ_2, (38) as the basis for Σ_3, etc., we can show that in the resulting expression

$$P^{-1}AP = B_1 + B_2 + \cdots + B_t,$$

every matrix B_i is non-derogatory and is of the type (35).

To make the notation less complex, let us assume that

$$n = 9, \quad m(x) = [l(x)]^2, \quad l(x) = l_0 + l_1 x + l_2 x^2 + x^3,$$
$$P = [\phi, A\phi, A^2\phi, \phi_1, A\phi_1, A^2\phi_1, \psi, A\psi, A^2\psi]$$

where ϕ is a vector in the null space of $[l(A)]^2$ which is not in the null space of $l(A)$, where $\phi_1 = l(A) \cdot \phi$, and where ψ is a vector determined as in §46. Then (see §45)

$$AP = [A\phi, A^2\phi, -l_0\phi - l_1 A\phi - l_2 A^2\phi + \phi_1, A\phi_1, A^2\phi_1,$$
$$-l_0\phi_1 - l_1 A\phi_1 - l_2 A^2\phi_1, A\psi, A^2\psi, -l_0\psi - l_1 A\psi - l_2 A^2\psi]$$
$$= [\phi, A\phi, A^2\phi, \phi_1, A\phi_1, A^2\phi_1, \psi, A\psi, A^2\psi]B = PB$$

where

$$(39) \quad B = \begin{bmatrix}
0 & 0 & -l_0 & 0 & 0 & 0 & 0 & 0 & 0 \\
1 & 0 & -l_1 & 0 & 0 & 0 & 0 & 0 & 0 \\
0 & 1 & -l_2 & 0 & 0 & 0 & 0 & 0 & 0 \\
0 & 0 & 1 & 0 & 0 & -l_0 & 0 & 0 & 0 \\
0 & 0 & 0 & 1 & 0 & -l_1 & 0 & 0 & 0 \\
0 & 0 & 0 & 0 & 1 & -l_2 & 0 & 0 & 0 \\
0 & 0 & 0 & 0 & 0 & 0 & 0 & 0 & -l_0 \\
0 & 0 & 0 & 0 & 0 & 0 & 1 & 0 & -l_1 \\
0 & 0 & 0 & 0 & 0 & 0 & 0 & 1 & -l_2
\end{bmatrix}.$$

It should be noted that this matrix differs from (35) only in having a 0 instead of a 1 in the 7th row and 6th column. That is, (39) is a direct sum of a matrix of type (35) of order 6 and another of order 3.

In general, we shall have

$$P^{-1}AP = B_1 \dotplus B_2 \dotplus \cdots \dotplus B_t$$

where each matrix B_i is of type (35), and hence is non-derogatory (see §45). The minimum function of B_1 is $[l(x)]^h$ (see §46), the minimum function of B_2 is $[l(x)]^k$ (see §46), the minimum function of B_3 is $[l(x)]^e$ (see §47), etc.

THEOREM 67. *If the matrix A has the minimum function* $[l(x)]^h$ *where* $l(x)$ *is irreducible, A is similar to a direct sum of non-derogatory matrices each of which has as its minimum function a divisor of* $[l(x)]^h$. *Each of these non-derogatory matrices is of type* (35).

By combining this result with Theorem 62, we have the general structure theorem:

THEOREM 68. *Let A be a matrix whose minimum function is*

$$m(x) = [l_1(x)]^{h_1} \cdot [l_2(x)]^{h_2} \cdots [l_k(x)]^{h_k}.$$

Then A is similar to a direct sum of non-derogatory matrices each of which has as its minimum function a divisor of one of the polynomials $[l_i(x)]^{h_i}$. *Each matrix in this direct sum is of the type* (35).

A matrix of the form described in the above theorem will be said to be in the *rational canonical form* for a matrix under similarity transformations.

CHAPTER VII

ELEMENTARY DIVISORS

49. Equivalence of matrices. Consider the set of all polynomials in x with coefficients in a field F. This set is called the *polynomial domain* of F, and is denoted by $F[x]$.

The domain $F[x]$ has many of the properties of the set of rational integers. It is closed under addition, subtraction and multiplication, but not under division. Those polynomials which are divisors of 1 are called *units*, and it is clear that the units of $F[x]$ are the polynomials of degree zero—that is, the numbers $\neq 0$ of F.

Those polynomials which are neither 0 nor units fall into two classes, *prime* or *irreducible* polynomials, and *composite* or *reducible* polynomials. Every reducible polynomial can be represented as the product of a finite number of irreducible polynomials and, except for unit factors and the order of the factors, this representation is unique. Two polynomials whose quotient is a unit are said to be *associated*.

A matrix P with elements in $F[x]$ is called *unimodular* if it has an inverse whose elements are likewise in $F[x]$. Clearly $P \cdot P^{-1} = I$ implies

$$d(P) \cdot d(P^{-1}) = 1.$$

If P and P^{-1} have elements in $F[x]$, both $d(P)$ and $d(P^{-1})$ are in $F[x]$ and are units. If, conversely, $d(P)$ is a unit, the elements of P^{-1} are in $F[x]$. Thus P is unimodular if and only if its determinant is a unit of $F[x]$. [since $P^{-1} = \frac{\mathrm{adj}\ P}{d(P)}$]

Two matrices A and B with elements in $F[x]$ are said

137

to be *equivalent* in $F[x]$ if unimodular matrices P and Q exist such that

$$B = PAQ.$$

Clearly the above equation implies

$$A = P^{-1}BQ^{-1}$$

so that equivalence is a symmetric relation. If also $C = RBS$ where R and S are unimodular, then

$$C = RPAQS.$$

Since RP and QS are unimodular, A and C are equivalent. Thus equivalence is transitive.

The theory of elementary transformations applies *mutatis mutandis* to matrices with polynomial elements. The three types are:

Type I: The interchange of two rows or of two columns.

Type II: The multiplication of the elements of any row, or column, by the same unit.

Type III: The addition to any row, or column, of a multiple by a polynomial of $F[x]$ of another row, or column.

The inverse of each elementary transformation is an elementary transformation of the same type. A transformation of Type I merely changes the sign of the determinant of the matrix; one of Type II multiplies the determinant by the unit; while a transformation of Type III leaves the determinant unchanged. Thus a unimodular matrix is transformed into a unimodular matrix by every elementary transformation.

Every elementary transformation on the rows (columns) of a matrix A can be accomplished by multiplying A on the left (right) by a unimodular matrix. The proof is similar to the proof of Theorem 13.

The theory connected with the Hermite canonical form may be carried over with only slight modifications. If A is a square matrix, there exists a non-singular matrix P which is a product of elementary matrices such that PA is triangular with every diagonal element either 0 or a polynomial with leading coefficient 1; if the diagonal element in any row is 0, the entire row is 0; if the diagonal element in any column is of degree d, every other element of the column is 0 or of degree $<d$ with leading coefficient 1. This form is unique.

Since the Hermite form of a unimodular matrix is I, it follows as in Theorem 20 that every unimodular matrix is equal to a product of elementary matrices.

50. Invariant factors. Let A be a matrix whose elements are polynomials of $F[x]$, and let

$$B_1^{(k)}, B_2^{(k)}, B_3^{(k)}, \cdots$$

be all of the k-rowed minor determinants which can be formed from A. If A is of rank r, and if $k \leqq r$, there will exist at least one k-rowed minor determinant of A which is not equal to zero, so that there will exist a (non-zero) greatest common divisor of all the k-rowed minor determinants of A. This polynomial, chosen so that the coefficient of the leading term is 1, we shall call the k-th *determinantal divisor* of A, and denote by d_k.

If k exceeds the rank r of A, there exists no determinantal divisor d_k.

We know that, if A and B are equivalent, they have the same rank r. We shall show that they have the same determinantal divisors

$$d_1, d_2, \cdots, d_r.$$

Let

$$A_1^{(k)}, A_2^{(k)}, A_3^{(k)}, \cdots, \qquad B_1^{(k)}, B_2^{(k)}, B_3^{(k)}, \cdots$$

be the k-rowed minor determinants of A and B, respectively, and let d_k be the g.c.d. of the $A^{(k)}_i$ and d'_k be the g.c.d. of the $B^{(k)}_i$.

Let B be obtained from A by an elementary transformation of Type I. Then the $B^{(k)}_i$ are merely a permutation of the $A^{(k)}_i$ so that $d'_k = d_k$.

Let B be obtained from A by an elementary transformation of Type II. Then each determinant $B^{(k)}_i$ is either equal to the corresponding $A^{(k)}_i$ or differs from it by a unit factor. Thus $d'_k = d_k$.

Let B be obtained from A by an elementary transformation of Type III. Then each $B^{(k)}_i$ is either equal to the corresponding $A^{(k)}_i$ or is of the form

$$B_i^{(k)} = A_i^{(k)} + m A_j^{(k)}$$

where m is in $F[x]$. Clearly d_k is a divisor of all the $B^{(k)}_i$ and hence is a divisor of d'_k. Since the inverse of an elementary transformation of Type III is an elementary transformation of Type III, d'_k is a divisor of d_k and, since each has 1 for its leading coefficient, $d_k = d'_k$.

Since every unimodular matrix can be written as a product of elementary matrices, it follows that, if $B = PAQ$ where P and Q are unimodular, A and B have the same determinantal divisors $d_1, d_2, \cdots, d_r$.

If $A_i^{(k+1)}$ is a $(k+1)$-rowed minor determinant of A, we can by the Laplace expansion (Theorem 35) express it as a linear combination of k-rowed minor determinants of A. Hence d_k is a divisor of d_{k+1} for $k = 1, 2, \cdots, r-1$. The quotients

$$\frac{d_r}{d_{r-1}} = h_r, \frac{d_{r-1}}{d_{r-2}} = h_{r-1}, \cdots, \frac{d_2}{d_1} = h_2, \; d_1 = h_1$$

are therefore polynomials in x, with leading coefficients

equal to 1, which determine the determinantal divisors uniquely, and are in turn uniquely defined by them. These polynomials

$$h_1, h_2, \cdots, h_r,$$

none of which can be 0, are called the *invariant factors* of A.

We have proved

THEOREM 69. *If two matrices with elements in $F[x]$ are equivalent, they have the same determinantal divisors and the same invariant factors.*

51. A canonical form. Let A be a square matrix of order n and rank r with elements in $F[x]$. By means of elementary transformations on the rows and columns we may reduce A to a canonical form.

Let

$$A = \begin{bmatrix} a_{11} & a_{12} \cdots a_{1n} \\ a_{21} & a_{22} \cdots a_{2n} \\ \cdot & \cdot \cdot \cdot \cdot \cdot \\ a_{n1} & a_{n2} \cdots a_{nn} \end{bmatrix}.$$

If $r>0$, we can permute the rows and columns so that $a_{11}\neq0$ and the degree of a_{11} does not exceed the degree of any element of A. Let a_{1i} be any element of the first row $\neq a_{11}$. We may write

$$a_{1i} = q \cdot a_{11} + t$$

where either $t=0$ or t is of lower degree than a_{11}. Then if we subtract from the i-th column q times the first column, the new element in the place of a_{1i} will be t. If $t\neq0$, it can be moved into the a_{11} position and we may start again with an a_{11} of lower degree. In a finite number of steps we shall have a new matrix A with $a_{11}\neq0$ and every other element of the first row and of the first column equal to 0.

Unless a_{11} divides every element of this new matrix A, its degree can be still further reduced. Suppose the element in the (i, j)-position in the new matrix A to be

$$a_{ij} = q \cdot a_{11} + t$$

where t is of lower degree than a_{11}. If we add the ith row to the first row, we have placed this polynomial a_{ij} in the a_{1j} position, and as before we can replace a_{11} by t.

We may now assume that A has the form

$$A_1 = \begin{bmatrix} a_{11} & 0 & 0 & \cdots & 0 \\ 0 & a_{22} & a_{23} & \cdots & a_{2n} \\ 0 & a_{32} & a_{33} & \cdots & a_{3n} \\ \cdot & \cdot & \cdot & \cdot & \cdot \\ 0 & a_{n2} & a_{n3} & \cdots & a_{nn} \end{bmatrix}$$

where a_{11} is a divisor of every element of A. If $r > 1$, we may now ignore the first row and first column, and in a similar manner reduce A to the form

$$A_2 = \begin{bmatrix} a_{11} & 0 & 0 & 0 & \cdots & 0 \\ 0 & a_{22} & 0 & 0 & \cdots & 0 \\ 0 & 0 & a_{33} & a_{34} & \cdots & a_{3n} \\ 0 & 0 & a_{43} & a_{44} & \cdots & a_{4n} \\ \cdot & \cdot & \cdot & \cdot & \cdot & \cdot \\ 0 & 0 & a_{n3} & a_{n4} & \cdots & a_{nn} \end{bmatrix}$$

where a_{22} is a divisor of every element of A_2 except perhaps a_{11}. Since A_2 was obtained from A_1 by elementary transformations, every element of A_2 is equal to a linear homogeneous function of the elements of A_1. Since a_{11} is a divisor of every element of A_1, it is a divisor of every element of A_2.

By a continuation of this process we eventually obtain

$$A_r = \begin{bmatrix} a_{11} & 0 & \cdots & 0 & \cdots & 0 \\ 0 & a_{22} & \cdots & 0 & \cdots & 0 \\ \cdot & \cdot & \cdot & \cdot & \cdot & \cdot \\ 0 & 0 & \cdots & a_{rr} & \cdots & 0 \\ \cdot & \cdot & \cdot & \cdot & \cdot & \cdot \\ 0 & 0 & \cdots & 0 & \cdots & 0 \end{bmatrix}$$

where a_{ii} divides $a_{i+1,i+1}$. If the rank of A is r, every element of A_r whose row and column indices exceed r must be 0, for otherwise a minor determinant of order $r+1$ could be formed which would not be equal to 0.

Since a_{11} divides a_{22}, a_{22} divides a_{33}, etc., it is clear that the determinantal divisors are

$$d_r = a_{11}a_{22} \cdots a_{rr}, \; d_{r-1} = a_{11}a_{22} \cdots a_{r-1,r-1}, \; \cdots, \; d_1 = a_{11}$$

and that the invariant factors are

$$h_1 = a_{11}, \; h_2 = a_{22}, \cdots, \; h_r = a_{rr}.$$

We have proved

THEOREM 70. *Every matrix A of order n and rank r with the invariant factors $h_1, h_2, \cdots, h_r$ is equivalent to the diagonal matrix*

$$\begin{bmatrix} h_1 & 0 & \cdots & 0 & \cdots & 0 \\ 0 & h_2 & \cdots & 0 & \cdots & 0 \\ \cdot & \cdot & \cdot & \cdot & \cdot & \cdot \\ 0 & 0 & \cdots & h_r & \cdots & 0 \\ \cdot & \cdot & \cdot & \cdot & \cdot & \cdot \\ 0 & 0 & \cdots & 0 & \cdots & 0 \end{bmatrix}.$$

COROLLARY 70. *Each invariant factor h_i is a divisor of the next invariant factor h_{i+1}.*

We may now prove the important theorem,

THEOREM 71. *Two matrices A and B of order n with elements in $F[x]$ are equivalent if and only if they have the same invariant factors.*

By Theorem 69 two equivalent matrices have the same invariant factors. By Theorem 70 two matrices having the same invariant factors are equivalent to the same matrix and hence are equivalent to each other.

52. Elementary divisors. Let $l_1, l_2, \cdots, l_p$ be the irreducible polynomials, each with leading coefficient 1, which divide at least one of the invariant factors h_i. It is then possible to write

$$h_i = l_1^{e_{i1}} l_2^{e_{i2}} \cdots l_p^{e_{ip}}$$

where each exponent e_{ij} is a positive integer or 0. The prime power factors

$$l_1^{e_{11}}, \cdots, l_p^{e_{1p}}, \cdots, l_1^{e_{r1}}, \cdots, l_p^{e_{rp}}$$

whose exponents are actually greater than zero are called the *elementary divisors* of the matrix A.

It is obvious that the invariant factors determine the elementary divisors uniquely. It is true, conversely, that the elementary divisors (without regard for their order) and the integer r determine the invariant factors uniquely. Since h_r is divisible by each of the other h's, h_r is the product of the highest power of l_1 by the highest power of $l_2 \cdots$ by the highest power of l_p which occur among the elementary divisors. As these are used, they may be crossed out. Then h_{r-1} is the product of the highest power of l_1 which remains by the highest power of l_2 which remains, etc. After the elementary divisors are all used up, the remaining h's are equal to 1.

Thus if $r = 4$ and the elementary divisors are

$$x^3, \ x^3, \ x, \ (x-1)^3, \ (x-1)^2,$$

the invariant factors are

$$h_4 = x^3(x-1)^3, \quad h_3 = x^3(x-1)^2, \quad h_2 = x, \quad h_1 = 1.$$

We have proved

THEOREM 72. *Two matrices have the same invariant factors if and only if they have the same rank and the same elementary divisors.*

It is not immediately evident that the elementary divisors are more useful than the invariant factors. Their introduction is thoroughly justified, however, by the following theorem.

THEOREM 73. *If A is equivalent to the matrix*

$$\begin{bmatrix} g_1 & 0 & \cdots & 0 & \cdots & 0 \\ 0 & g_2 & \cdots & 0 & \cdots & 0 \\ \cdot & \cdot & \cdot & \cdot & \cdot & \cdot \\ 0 & 0 & \cdots & g_r & \cdots & 0 \\ \cdot & \cdot & \cdot & \cdot & \cdot & \cdot \\ 0 & 0 & \cdots & 0 & \cdots & 0 \end{bmatrix}$$

where each $g_i \neq 0$ but it is not necessarily true that g_i divides g_{i+1}, then the prime power factors of the g's are the elementary divisors of A.

Let l be any prime factor of any one of the g's, and arrange the g's according to ascending powers of this prime factor. That is,

$$g_{i_1} = f_1 l^{k_1}, \ g_{i_2} = f_2 l^{k_2}, \ \cdots, \ g_{i_r} = f_r l^{k_r}$$

where the f's are prime to l and

$$k_1 \leqq k_2 \leqq \cdots \leqq k_r.$$

It is evident that the highest power of l which divides the determinantal divisor d_i has the exponent

$$k_1 + k_2 + \cdots + k_i.$$

Hence the highest power of l which divides the invariant factor h_i is l^{k_i}, so that for every i for which $k_i \geqq 1$ this prime power is an elementary divisor of A. If this argument is repeated for every prime which divides a g, we shall see that every prime power factor of every g is an elementary divisor of A, and all elementary divisors of A are thus obtained.

This theorem is of great practical importance. Consider the matrix

$$A = \begin{bmatrix} x^2(x-1)^2 & 0 & 0 \\ 0 & x(x-1)^3 & 0 \\ 0 & 0 & x \end{bmatrix}.$$

The elementary divisors are

$$x^2, \ (x-1)^2, \ x, \ (x-1)^3, \ x$$

so that the invariant factors are

$$h_3 = x^2(x-1)^3, \quad h_2 = x(x-1)^2, \quad h_1 = x.$$

Hence A is equivalent to the matrix

$$\begin{bmatrix} x & 0 & 0 \\ 0 & x(x-1)^2 & 0 \\ 0 & 0 & x^2(x-1)^3 \end{bmatrix}.$$

The actual reduction of A to this form would entail considerable calculation.

53. Elementary divisors of a direct sum. The following generalization of Theorem 73 will prove useful.

THEOREM 74. *If*
$$A = A_1 \dotplus A_2 \dotplus \cdots \dotplus A_t,$$
the elementary divisors of A are the elementary divisors of all the matrices A_i taken together.

By Theorem 71 we can find non-singular matrices P_i and Q_i such that
$$P_i A_i Q_i = A_i'$$
where A_i' is diagonal. Define
$$P = P_1 \dotplus P_2 \dotplus \cdots \dotplus P_t, \qquad Q = Q_1 \dotplus Q_2 \dotplus \cdots \dotplus Q_t.$$
By (d) of §42,
$$PAQ = A_1' \dotplus A_2' \dotplus \cdots \dotplus A_t' = A',$$
and by (g) of §42, both P and Q are non-singular. Clearly A' is diagonal. By Theorem 73 the elementary divisors of the A_i are the prime power factors of the diagonal elements of the A_i', and by this same theorem the elementary divisors of A are the prime power factors of all the A_i' taken together.

Consider the canonical form (35) which was of so much importance in Chapter VI. Its characteristic matrix is

$$(40) \quad
\begin{bmatrix}
-x & 0 & -l_0 & 0 & 0 & 0 & 0 & 0 & 0 \\
1 & -x & -l_1 & 0 & 0 & 0 & 0 & 0 & 0 \\
0 & 1 & -l_2-x & 0 & 0 & 0 & 0 & 0 & 0 \\
0 & 0 & 1 & -x & 0 & -l_0 & 0 & 0 & 0 \\
0 & 0 & 0 & 1 & -x & -l_1 & 0 & 0 & 0 \\
0 & 0 & 0 & 0 & 1 & -l_2-x & 0 & 0 & 0 \\
0 & 0 & 0 & 0 & 0 & 1 & -x & 0 & -l_0 \\
0 & 0 & 0 & 0 & 0 & 0 & 1 & -x & -l_1 \\
0 & 0 & 0 & 0 & 0 & 0 & 0 & 1 & -l_2-x
\end{bmatrix}$$

whose determinant is the 9th determinantal divisor d_9. By the Laplace expansion (Theorem 35)

$$d_9 = \begin{vmatrix} -x & 0 & -l_0 \\ 1 & -x & -l_1 \\ 0 & 1 & -l_2 - x \end{vmatrix}^3$$

and by §31,

$$d_9 = [l(x)]^3.$$

Now if we cross out the first row and last column of the matrix (40), we obtain a matrix having nothing but 0's below the main diagonal and 1's in this diagonal. The determinant of this matrix is 1, so that the 8th determinantal divisor is $d_8 = 1$. In fact

$$d_1 = d_2 = \cdots = d_8 = 1.$$

Thus the invariant factors are

$$h_1 = h_2 = \cdots = h_8 = 1, \qquad h_9 = [l(x)]^3$$

and the only elementary divisor is $[l(x)]^3$.

In general, we have

THEOREM 75. *Every matrix of the form* (35) *has a characteristic matrix with a single elementary divisor. If* $l(x)$ *is of degree* j *and if* (35) *is of order* jh, *this elementary divisor is* $[l(x)]^h$. *The canonical form of Type* (35) *is uniquely defined by its elementary divisor.*

54. Similar matrices. Let A and B be matrices with elements in the field F which are similar in F. That is, there exists a non-singular matrix P with elements in F such that

$$B = P^{-1}AP.$$

Then

$$P^{-1}(A - xI)P = P^{-1}AP - P^{-1}xIP = B - xI$$

so that the characteristic matrices of A and B are equivalent in the domain $F[x]$. It is then evident from Theorem 72 that, if A and B are similar in F, their characteristic matrices are matrices with elements in $F[x]$ which have the same invariant factors. The converse, which is not so evident, will now be proved.

THEOREM 76. *Two matrices A and B with elements in F are similar in F if and only if their characteristic matrices are equivalent in $F[x]$—that is, if and only if they have the same invariant factors.*

The necessity of the condition has just been proved.

In Chapter VI it was proved that every matrix A with elements in F is similar to a direct sum of matrices A_i of Type (35). By Theorem 75, each matrix of Type (35) has a single elementary divisor and is uniquely determined by it. By Theorem 74, the collection of these elementary divisors of the matrices A_i is the set of elementary divisors of A. The order of the components A_i in the direct sum can be arranged at will by a similarity transformation so that, if $A - xI$ and $B - xI$ have the same elementary divisors, it must be true that their canonical forms described in Theorem 68 can be taken to be identical. Then A and B are similar in F.

It is now clear that two matrices with the same minimum function are not necessarily similar. Thus let A be a matrix with elements in F whose minimum function is

$$m(x) = [l_1(x)]^{h_1} \cdot [l_2(x)]^{h_2} \cdots [l_k(x)]^{h_k}$$

where the polynomials $l_i(x)$ are irreducible and relatively prime in pairs. The elementary divisors of $A - xI$ are the factors $[l_i(x)]^{h_i}$ and divisors of these factors.

Consider for a moment the matrix considered in §45 of order n and index μ having the minimum function

$$m(x) = [l(x)]^h \qquad\qquad \mu = jh,$$

so that $l(x)$ was of degree j. We chose the vector ϕ to be any vector in the null space of $[l(A)]^h$ which was not in the null space of $[l(A)]^{h-1}$, and by means of ϕ constructed a subspace Σ_1 of the total space S. Then in §46 we chose a vector ψ such that $[l(A)]^k \cdot \psi$ was in Σ_1, but $[l(A)]^{k-1} \cdot \psi$ was not in Σ_1, and such that k was maximal, and constructed another subspace Σ_2. We then showed that $[l(x)]^k$ was another elementary divisor of $A - xI$. Then in §47 we chose another vector χ such that $[l(A)]^e \cdot \chi$ was in $\Sigma_1 \cup \Sigma_2$, while $[l(A)]^{e-1} \cdot \chi$ was not, and such that e was maximal. This led to another elementary divisor $[l(x)]^e$, etc.

In §§45–47 it appeared that the vector ψ depended upon the choice of ϕ, that the vector χ depended upon the choice of both ϕ and ψ, etc. It seemed probable that the value of k also depended upon what vector ϕ was selected, and that e depended upon both ϕ and ψ. We now see that the integers $h, k, e, \cdots$ are invariants of the canonical form and thus are independent of the choice (within their range of definition) of the vectors $\phi, \psi, \chi, \cdots$.

These integers $h, k, e, \cdots$ constitute the *Segrè characteristic* of A relative to the prime factor $l(x)$ of the minimum equation.

55. The Weyr characteristic. Let A be a matrix with elements in F having the minimum function

$$m(x) = [l_1(x)]^{h_1} \cdot [l_2(x)]^{h_2} \cdots [l_k(x)]^{h_k}$$

where the $l_i(x)$ are irreducible and distinct. Let

$$g_{i1}, \; g_{i1} + g_{i2}, \; g_{i1} + g_{i2} + g_{i3}, \cdots, \; g_{i1} + g_{i2} + \cdots + g_{ih_i}$$

denote the nullities (see §40) of the respective matrices

$$l_i(A), \; [l_i(A)]^2, \; [l_i(A)]^3, \cdots, \; [l_i(A)]^{h_i}.$$

Since the nullity of a matrix is its order minus its rank, the integer g_{ik} indicates the drop in rank between the matrix $[l_i(A)]^{k-1}$ and the matrix $[l_i(A)]^k$.

THEOREM 77. *Every integer g_{ik} is divisible by the degree j_i of the irreducible polynomial $l_i(x)$.*

It is immediately evident from (30) of §41 that these integers g_{ik} are invariant under similarity transformations upon A. By Theorem 68, A is similar to a direct sum of non-derogatory matrices each of which has a minimum function of the type $[l(x)]^k$. That is,

$$A \overset{\mathrm{s}}{=} A_1 + \cdots + A_t + A_{t+1} + \cdots + A_v$$

where $A_1, \cdots, A_t$ have minimum functions which are powers of $l_i(x)$, while $A_{t+1}, \cdots, A_v$ have minimum functions which are prime to $l_i(x)$. By (30) and (k) of §42,

$$[l_i(A)]^k \overset{\mathrm{s}}{=} [l_i(A_1)]^k + \cdots + [l_i(A_t)]^k$$
$$+ [l_i(A_{t+1})]^k + \cdots + [l_i(A_v)]^k.$$

By Theorem 44 each of the matrices

$$[l_i(A_{t+1})]^k, \cdots, [l_i(A_v)]^k$$

is non-singular and hence of nullity zero for every value of k, while by Corollary 57 each of the matrices

$$[l_i(A_1)]^k, \cdots, [l_i(A_i)]^k$$

is of nullity $j_i k$ if $j_i k$ is less than or equal to its order, otherwise it is a zero matrix.

The nullity of a direct sum is obviously equal to the sum of the nullities of the components (see (h) of §42), whence it follows that the nullity of $[l_i(A)]^k$ is divisible by j_i, and so therefore is every integer g_{ik}.

Set $g_{ik} = w_{ik}j_i$. The integers

$$w_{i1}, w_{i2}, \cdots, w_{ih_i}$$

constitute the *Weyr characteristic* of the matrix A relative to the irreducible factor $l_i(x)$ of its minimum function.

THEOREM 78. *The Segrê characteristic and the Weyr characteristic of the matrix A relative to the same irreducible factor $l(x)$ of its minimum function are conjugate partitions of the same integer.*

The avoid elaborate notation we shall take a special example which is typical of the general situation. Let A have the Segrê characteristic (5, 4, 2, 2) relative to the irreducible factor $l(x)$ of degree j of its minimum function. Then

$$A \overset{s}{=} A_1 + A_2 + A_3 + A_4 + \cdots$$

where each of the A's is non-derogatory. The minimum functions of A_1, A_2, A_3, A_4 are by Theorem 68 respectively

$$[l(x)]^5, \quad [l(x)]^4, \quad [l(x)]^2, \quad [l(x)]^2,$$

while the matrices represented by dots have minimum functions which are prime to $l(x)$. Then for every i

$$[l(A)]^i \overset{s}{=} [l(A_1)]^i + [l(A_2)]^i + [l(A_3)]^i + [l(A_4)]^i + B_i$$

where B_i is a non-singular matrix. By Corollary 57

$$l(A_1), \ l(A_2), \ l(A_3), \ l(A_4)$$

are each of nullity j so that $g_1 = 4j$ and $w_1 = 4$. Then

$$[l(A_1)]^2, \ [l(A_2)]^2, \ [l(A_3)]^2, \ [l(A_4)]^2$$

are each of nullity $2j$ so that

$$g_1 + g_2 = 8j, \qquad w_2 = 4.$$

But the last two of the above matrices are 0 so that there is no further increase in nullity when the exponents of $l(A_3)$ and $l(A_4)$ are increased. Thus

$$g_1 + g_2 + g_3 = 10j, \qquad g_1 + g_2 + g_3 + g_4 = 12j,$$
$$w_3 = 2, \qquad w_4 = 2.$$

Now $[l(A_2)]^4 = 0$ so that

$$g_1 + g_2 + g_3 + g_4 + g_5 = 13j, \qquad w_5 = 1.$$

There are no further non-zero w's.

Now let us arrange the integers of the Segré characteristic as rows of dots,

$$
\begin{array}{ccccc}
\bullet & \bullet & \bullet & \bullet & \bullet \\
\bullet & \bullet & \bullet & \bullet & \\
\bullet & \bullet & & & \\
\bullet & & & &
\end{array}
$$

The numbers of dots in the columns, namely $(4, 4, 2, 2, 1)$, are the numbers of the conjugate partition of 13. That they constitute the Weyr characteristic is obvious, for the increase in nullity in passing from $[l(A)]^{i-1}$ to $[l(A)]^i$ is equal to the number of matrices A_i whose minimum functions are powers of $l(x)$ having an exponent $\geq i$—that is, the number of dots in the ith column of the above display.

A really typical numerical example would require a matrix of quite high order, but the example of §32 will be of some assistance. We have

$$A = \begin{bmatrix} 7 & 4 & -1 \\ 4 & 7 & -1 \\ -4 & -4 & 4 \end{bmatrix}$$

which is of rank 3 and whose characteristic function is

$$f(x) = (x - 3)^2(x - 12).$$

The matrix

$$A - 3I = \begin{bmatrix} 4 & 4 & -1 \\ 4 & 4 & -1 \\ -4 & -4 & 1 \end{bmatrix}$$

is of rank 1 so that $g_{11} = 2$ and $w_{11} = 2$. Since $[A - 3I]^2$ is also of rank 1, w_{12} does not exist.

Furthermore

$$A - 12I = \begin{bmatrix} -5 & 4 & -1 \\ 4 & -5 & -1 \\ -4 & -4 & -8 \end{bmatrix}$$

is of rank 2, and so is its square. Thus $g_{21} = w_{21} = 1$.

The conjugate partition of 2 is $1 + 1$, and the conjugate partition of 1 is 1. Thus A has the elementary divisors

$$x - 3, \qquad x - 3, \qquad x - 12$$

and the invariant factors

$$h_3 = (x - 3)(x - 12), \quad h_2 = x - 3, \quad h_1 = 1.$$

The canonical form is

$$\begin{bmatrix} 3 & 0 & 0 \\ 0 & 3 & 0 \\ 0 & 0 & 12 \end{bmatrix}$$

and the minimum function is

$$m(x) = h_3 = (x - 3)(x - 12).$$

56. Collineations. Since the early work in elementary divisor theory was motivated by projective geometry, it may not be out of place to see what the connections between these two topics are.

Referred to a system of trilinear homogeneous coordinates, the equations

$$x_1' = a_{11}x_1 + a_{12}x_2 + a_{13}x_3,$$
$$x_2' = a_{21}x_1 + a_{22}x_2 + a_{23}x_3,$$
$$x_3' = a_{31}x_1 + a_{32}x_2 + a_{33}x_3$$

define a *projective transformation* or *collineation* of the points of the projective plane. We shall assume that the elements a_{ij} as well as the x's belong to the real field R.

The above transformation may be written in the form

$$\xi' = A\xi$$

where ξ is the vector (x_1, x_2, x_3), $\xi' = (x_1', x_2', x_3')$ and $A = (a_{rs})$ is the matrix of the collineation. If $\xi'' = B\xi'$ is another collineation, then evidently

$$\xi'' = BA\xi$$

is the resultant collineation. The matrix of the resultant of two collineations, then, is equal to the product of the matrices of these collineations in reverse order. This is one way in which the concept of product of two matrices can be introduced.

Let us suppose that a new system of trilinear coordinates is chosen. Every point with coordinates (x_1, x_2, x_3) in the old coordinate system will have coordinates (y_1, y_2, y_3) in the new coordinate system, and vice versa. There will exist a set of equations

$$x_1 = t_{11}y_1 + t_{12}y_2 + t_{13}y_3,$$
$$x_2 = t_{21}y_1 + t_{22}y_2 + t_{23}y_3,$$
$$x_3 = t_{31}y_1 + t_{32}y_2 + t_{33}y_3$$

relating these sets of coordinates. If we denote (y_1, y_2, y_3) by η, these equations may be written

$$\xi = T\eta$$

where $T = (t_{rs})$ is non-singular. Conversely every non-singular matrix T defines a coordinate system.

The point (x_1', x_2', x_3') will also have coordinates (y_1', y_2', y_3') in the new coordinate system. Then

$$\xi' = T\eta', \qquad \eta' = (y_1', y_2', y_3').$$

That is,

$$T\eta' = \xi' = A\xi = AT\eta$$

so that

$$\eta' = T^{-1}AT\ \eta.$$

We have proved

THEOREM 79. *If a collineation has the matrix A in one trilinear homogeneous coordinate system, it has the similar* *matrix $T^{-1}AT$ in every such coordinate system; and conversely every matrix similar to A is the matrix of this collineation in some coordinate system.*

Two vectors are the homogeneous coordinates of the same point if and only if they are proportional. Thus (x_1, x_2, x_3) is left invariant by a collineation if and only if there exists a non-zero real number λ such that

$$x_1' = \lambda x_1, \qquad x_2' = \lambda x_2, \qquad x_3' = \lambda x_3.$$

Hence λ must satisfy the linear homogeneous equations

$$(41) \qquad \begin{aligned} (a_{11} - \lambda)x_1 + a_{12}x_2 + a_{13}x_3 &= 0, \\ a_{21}x_1 + (a_{22} - \lambda)x_2 + a_{23}x_3 &= 0, \\ a_{31}x_1 + a_{32}x_2 + (a_{33} - \lambda)x_3 &= 0. \end{aligned}$$

The number of solutions will depend upon the rank of the matrix

$$A - \lambda I.$$

In order that there may be any solution at all with (x_1, x_2, x_3) not all zero, it is necessary that λ be a solution of the characteristic equation

$$|A - \lambda I| = 0$$

of the matrix A.

If λ_1 is a characteristic root, then $A - \lambda_1 I$ is singular. If $A - \lambda_1 I$ is of rank 2, equations (41) with λ_1 substituted for λ have but one linearly independent solution, so that corresponding to λ_1 there is just one invariant point of the collineation. If, however, $A - \lambda_1 I$ is of rank 1, equations (41) have two non-proportional solutions

$$(a_1, a_2, a_3), \qquad (b_1, b_2, b_3),$$

and all vectors of the form

$$(ka_1 + lb_1, \ ka_2 + lb_2, \ ka_3 + lb_3)$$

are solutions where k and l are arbitrary. In this case there is a whole line of invariant points. If $A - \lambda_1 I$ is of rank 0, every point of the plane is invariant. Thus the number of invariant points depends upon the first component of the Weyr characteristic corresponding to each real linear factor of the characteristic equation of A.

In the plane case, which we have chosen,

$$| A - \lambda I | = 0$$

is a cubic equation and hence has at least one real root. If the other two roots are complex, there is just one invariant point. But if all three roots are real, there are various possibilities depending upon the elementary divisors of $A - \lambda I$.

Elementary Divisors	Segré Char.	Weyr Char.	Invariants.
$\lambda - \lambda_1, \ \lambda - \lambda_2, \ \lambda - \lambda_3$	$[1, 1, 1]$	$[1, 1, 1]$	3 *distinct pts.*
$\lambda - \lambda_1, \ \lambda - \lambda_1, \ \lambda - \lambda_2$	$[(1, 1), 1]$	$[2, 1]$	*line and pt.*
$\lambda - \lambda_1, \ \lambda - \lambda_1, \ \lambda - \lambda_1$	$[(1, 1, 1)]$	$[3]$	*the plane.*
$(\lambda - \lambda_1)^2, \ (\lambda - \lambda_2)$	$[2, 1]$	$[(1, 1), 1]$	2 *distinct pts.*
$(\lambda - \lambda_1)^2, \ (\lambda - \lambda_1)$	$[(2, 1)]$	$[(2, 1)]$	*one line*
$(\lambda - \lambda_1)^3$	$[3]$	$[(1, 1, 1)]$	*one point.*

In the second case, for instance, there are two distinct characteristic roots. Relative to the first root there are two elementary divisors $\lambda - \lambda_1$, $\lambda - \lambda_1$, so that the Segré characteristic is (1,1). Relative to the second characteristic root the Segré characteristic is 1. The complete Segré characteristic, then, may be written $[(1, 1), 1]$. The conjugate partition of $(1, 1)$ is 2 so that the complete Weyr characteristic is $[2, 1]$. The integer 2 indicates that $A - \lambda_1 I$ is of nullity 2 or rank 1, so that there is a line of invariant points corresponding to the characteristic root λ_1. Since $A - \lambda_2 I$ is of rank 2, it leads to an invariant point which is not on the line of invariant points. The other cases are similar.

CHAPTER VIII

ORTHOGONAL TRANSFORMATIONS

57. Orthogonal matrices. Consider the ordinary three-dimensional euclidean space with two sets x, y, z and x', y', z' of orthogonal axes having the same origin. If a point has the coordinates (a, b, c) relative to the first set of axes, and the coordinates (a', b', c') relative to the second set, it is true that

$$a' = a \cos (x'x) + b \cos (x'y) + c \cos (x'z),$$
$$b' = a \cos (y'x) + b \cos (y'y) + c \cos (y'z),$$
$$c' = a \cos (z'x) + b \cos (z'y) + c \cos (z'z)$$

where $\cos (x'x)$ is the cosine of the angle between the x-axis and the x'-axis, etc.

The matrix

$$\begin{bmatrix} \cos (x'x) & \cos (x'y) & \cos (x'z) \\ \cos (y'x) & \cos (y'y) & \cos (y'z) \\ \cos (z'x) & \cos (z'y) & \cos (z'z) \end{bmatrix}$$

has some distinctive properties. The elements of each row are the direction cosines of one of the new coordinate axes relative to the old axes so that the sum of the squares of the elements of each row is 1. Since the axes are mutually perpendicular, the inner product of any row vector by any other row vector is zero. Moreover the elements of each column are the direction cosines of one of the old coordinate axes relative to the new system, so that the sum of the squares of the elements of each column is 1, and the inner product of two different column vectors is 0.

In general, a matrix with elements in a field F is called an *orthogonal matrix* if its transpose is equal to its inverse—that is, A is orthogonal if $AA^T = I$. This implies that A is non-singular, and that

$$\sum_{i=1}^{n} a_{ri} a_{si} = \delta_{rs}.$$

This means that the sum of the squares of the elements of each row vector is 1, while the inner product of two different row vectors is 0. The above conditions are likewise sufficient that A be orthogonal.

Since $A^T = A^{-1}$, it is also true, if A is orthogonal, that $A^T A = I$. That is,

$$\sum_{i=1}^{n} a_{ir} a_{is} = \delta_{rs}.$$

Hence the sum of the squares of the elements of each column vector is 1, and the inner product of two different column vectors is zero. These conditions also characterize an orthogonal matrix.

An orthogonal matrix of order n, then, may be thought of as a transformation in n-dimensional euclidean space from one set of mutually orthogonal axes to another such set having the same origin.

The product of two orthogonal matrices is orthogonal. For if

$$AA^T = I, \qquad BB^T = I,$$

then

$$(AB)(AB)^T = ABB^T A^T = AA^T = I.$$

The inverse of an orthogonal matrix is orthogonal, for if $AA^T = I$,

$$(A^{-1})^T A^{-1} = (A^T)^{-1} A^{-1} = (AA^T)^{-1} = I.$$

Clearly the identity matrix I is orthogonal. Thus the orthogonal matrices of order n form a group relative to multiplication.

58. Orthogonal bases. Two vectors

$$\phi = (v_1, v_2, \cdots, v_n), \qquad \omega = (w_1, w_2, \cdots, w_n)$$

are defined to be *orthogonal* if their inner product

$$\phi \cdot \omega = v_1 w_1 + v_2 w_2 + \cdots + v_n w_n$$

is equal to zero. (See §§6, 7.) This definition is purely formal, but it includes an important special case. If S is an n-dimensional euclidean space, and if the components of the vectors are relative to n mutually perpendicular unit vectors $\epsilon_1, \epsilon_2, \cdots, \epsilon_n$, each of unit length, then $\phi \cdot \omega = 0$ means that ϕ and ω are perpendicular to each other.

Let us investigate the possibility that a vector ϕ be orthogonal to itself. This would entail

$$v_1^2 + v_2^2 + \cdots + v_n^2 = 0$$

and is a phenomenon which can easily occur in a field such as the complex field where the vector $(1, i)$, for instance, is orthogonal to itself.* In order to avoid this embarrassing situation, we must assume that F is a formally real field—that is, that every relation

$$v_1^2 + v_2^2 + \cdots + v_n^2 = 0$$

where the v's are in the field implies that $v_1 = v_2 = \cdots = v_n = 0$. If F is formally real, the only vector which is orthogonal to itself is the zero vector.

* In complex geometry the orthogonality condition is usually modified to be $\phi \cdot \bar{\omega} = 0$ so that only the zero vector is orthogonal to itself.

THEOREM 80. *Let* F *be formally real, and let* β_1, $\beta_2, \cdots, \beta_k$ *be any* k *vectors which span the space* S_k *of dimension* k. *For any value of* i, $1 < i \leqq k$, *it is possible to find a vector* β_i' *such that*

$$\beta_1, \cdots, \beta_{i-1}, \beta_i', \beta_{i+1}, \cdots, \beta_k$$

span S_k, *and such that*

$$\beta_j \cdot \beta_i' = 0 \qquad\qquad j = 1, 2, \cdots, i - 1.$$

Let us set

$$\beta_i' = \sum_{h=1}^{i} l_h \beta_h$$

where the coefficients $l_1, l_2, \cdots, l_i$ are to be determined so that

$$\beta_j \cdot \beta_i' = \sum_{h=1}^{i} l_h \beta_j \cdot \beta_h = 0 \qquad j = 1, 2, \cdots, i - 1.$$

The inner product $\beta_j \cdot \beta_h$ is in F so that the above condition is actually a system of $i - 1$ linear homogeneous equations in the i unknowns $l_1, l_2, \cdots, l_i$, which by Corollary 4 has a solution not composed entirely of 0's.

In order to show that the linear systems of vectors

$$\beta_1, \cdots, \beta_i, \cdots, \beta_k, \qquad \beta_1, \cdots, \beta_i', \cdots, \beta_k$$

are linearly equivalent, it is sufficient to show that β_i can be written as a linear combination of the vectors

$$\beta_1, \cdots, \beta_{i-1}, \beta_i'.$$

That is, it is sufficient to show that $l_i \neq 0$. But if l_i were zero, we should have

$$\beta_i' = l_1\beta_1 + l_2\beta_2 + \cdots + l_{i-1}\beta_{i-1}.$$

Since β_i' is orthogonal to each of these vectors, it is orthogonal to every linear combination of them, and hence to itself. It must therefore be the zero vector, since F is formally real, and hence

$$l_1\beta_1 + l_2\beta_2 + \cdots + l_{i-1}\beta_{i-1} = 0.$$

But the vectors $\beta_1, \beta_2, \cdots, \beta_k$ are linearly independent since they span S_k of dimension k, so that we should have

$$l_1 = l_2 = \cdots = l_{i-1} = l_i = 0,$$

which is a contradiction. Thus $l_i \neq 0$.

A vector space S_k of dimension k is said to possess an *orthogonal basis*

$$\beta_1, \beta_2, \cdots, \beta_k$$

if the β's span S_k, and if

$$\beta_i \cdot \beta_j = 0 \qquad\qquad i \neq j.$$

THEOREM 81. *If F is formally real, and if S_k of dimension k is a subspace of the total vector space S of dimension n, an orthogonal basis*

$$\beta_1, \beta_2, \cdots, \beta_k, \cdots, \beta_n$$

can be found for S such that

$$\beta_1, \beta_2, \cdots, \beta_k$$

is an orthogonal basis for S_k.

Let $\gamma_1, \gamma_2, \cdots, \gamma_n$ be a basis for S such that $\gamma_1, \gamma_2, \cdots, \gamma_k$ is a basis for S_k. Take $\beta_1' = \gamma_1$. Then by means of Theorem 80 replace γ_2 by β_2' such that $\beta_1' \cdot \beta_2' = 0$. Then replace γ_3 by β_3' such that

$$\beta_1' \cdot \beta_3' = \beta_2' \cdot \beta_3' = 0.$$

Continue in this way until

$$\beta_1', \beta_2', \cdots, \beta_k'$$

is an orthogonal basis for S_k. Then continue in the same manner until an orthogonal basis

$$\beta_1', \beta_2', \cdots, \beta_n'$$

for S is obtained.

A vector $\phi = (v_1, v_2, \cdots, v_n)$ is said to be *normalized* if

$$v_1^2 + v_2^2 + \cdots + v_n^2 = 1.$$

Every vector $\phi \neq 0$ possesses a *normalizing factor k*, such that $k\phi$ is normalized, if $\sqrt{v_1^2 + v_2^2 + \cdots + v_n^2}$ is in the field F and is not 0. That F be formally real is necessary but not sufficient. Instead of attempting to delineate the most general type of field in which this condition is satisfied, we shall in the remainder of this chapter assume that F is the real field R.

COROLLARY 81. *If S_k of dimension k is a subspace of the total vector space S of dimension n over the real field, a normalized orthogonal basis*

$$\beta_1, \beta_2, \cdots, \beta_k, \cdots, \beta_n$$

can be found for S such that

$$\beta_1, \beta_2, \cdots, \beta_k$$

is a normalized orthogonal basis for S_k.

For if $\beta_1, \beta_2, \cdots, \beta_n$ is an orthogonal basis, $k_1\beta_1, k_2\beta_2, \cdots, k_n\beta_n$ is a normalized orthogonal basis where

$$k_i = 1/\sqrt{b_{i1}^2 + b_{i2}^2 + \cdots + b_{in}^2}, \quad \beta_i = (b_{i1}, b_{i2}, \cdots, b_{in}).$$

We now see that the row vectors (column vectors) of an orthogonal matrix form a set of normalized orthogonal vectors.

59. Symmetric matrices. A matrix is said to be *symmetric* if it is equal to its transpose. Thus $A = (a_{rs})$ is symmetric if $a_{rs} = a_{sr}$—e.g.,

$$\begin{bmatrix} 2 & 3 & -1 \\ 3 & 3 & 1 \\ -1 & 1 & -2 \end{bmatrix}.$$

If $A = A^T$, then $A^i = (A^T)^i = (A^i)^T$ so that A^i is also symmetric. Clearly the identity matrix I is symmetric, and kA is symmetric for every number k of the field. If A and B are symmetric,

$$(A + B)^T = A^T + B^T = A + B,$$

so that the sum of two symmetric matrices is symmetric. Thus if A is symmetric, so is $f(A)$ where $f(x)$ is any polynomial. In particular the inverse of a non-singular symmetric matrix is symmetric.

Two matrices A and B are said to be *orthogonally similar* if there exists an orthogonal matrix P such that

$$A = P^T B P.$$

We may then write $A \overset{\circ}{=} B$. It may readily be verified that orthogonal similarity is reflexive, symmetric and transitive. (See §41.) If B is symmetric and $A \overset{\circ}{=} B$, then A is also symmetric. For if $A = P^T B P$, then

$$A^T = P^T B^T P = P^T B P = A.$$

The theory of similarity is seriously handicapped when the transforming matrix is restricted to be orthogonal. To obtain any worth-while results, the transformed matrix must also be restricted. When the latter is taken to be symmetric, results of great geometrical importance can be obtained.

THEOREM 82. *Let A be a symmetric matrix with elements in any field F, such that the minimum function possesses two distinct linear factors $l_1(x)$ and $l_2(x)$ with coefficients in F. Let ϕ_1 be a vector of the null space of $l_1(A)$, and let ϕ_2 be a vector of the null space of $l_2(A)$. Then ϕ_1 and ϕ_2 are orthogonal.*

Let

$$l_1(x) = x_1 - x, \qquad l_2(x) = x_2 - x, \quad x_1 \neq x_2.$$

By Theorem 44, $l_1(A)$ is singular so that there exists a non-zero vector ϕ_1 such that

$$l_1(A) \cdot \phi_1 = 0, \qquad A\phi_1 = x_1\phi_1.$$

Similarly there exists a non-zero vector ϕ_2 such that $A\phi_2 = x_2\phi_2$. Hence

$$\phi_2 A\phi_1 = \phi_2 x_1\phi_1 = x_1\phi_2 \cdot \phi_1.$$

If $A = A^T$,

$$\phi_2 A\phi_1 = (\phi_2 A^T)\phi_1 = x_2\phi_2 \cdot \phi_1.$$

That is,

$$(x_1 - x_2)\phi_2 \cdot \phi_1 = 0.$$

If $x_1 \neq x_2$, $\phi_2 \cdot \phi_1 = 0$ so that ϕ_1 and ϕ_2 are orthogonal vectors.

A vector ϕ_1 such that $A\phi_1 = x_1\phi_1$ where x_1 is a characteristic root of A is commonly called a *pole* or *characteristic vector* of A.

COROLLARY 82. *The characteristic roots of a real symmetric matrix are all real.*

If A is real, its characteristic equation has real coefficients. The minimum function is a divisor of the characteristic function in the domain $R[x]$, so that the minimum equation of A also has real coefficients. The non-real roots of such an equation occur in conjugate pairs.

Suppose that x_1 is a non-real characteristic root of the real symmetric matrix A, and let ϕ_1 be a non-zero vector of the null space of $x_1 I - A$. Then

$$A\phi_1 = x_1\phi_1$$

and, since A is real,

$$A\bar{\phi}_1 = \bar{x}_1\bar{\phi}_1$$

where $\bar{x}_1$ is the complex conjugate of x_1. That is, $\bar{\phi}_1$ is a vector of the null space of $\bar{x}_1 I - A$. Since x_1 is not real, $\bar{x}_1 \neq x_1$, so that

$$\phi_1 \cdot \bar{\phi}_1 = 0$$

by Theorem 82. If $\phi_1 = (v_1, v_2, \cdots, v_n)$, then

$$\phi_1 \cdot \bar{\phi}_1 = v_1\bar{v}_1 + v_2\bar{v}_2 + \cdots + v_n\bar{v}_n = 0.$$

This implies that

$$v_1 = v_2 = \cdots = v_n = 0,$$

which is a contradiction, since we assumed $\phi_1 \neq 0$. Thus no non-real characteristic root of A can exist.

THEOREM 83. *The roots of the minimum equation of a real symmetric matrix are distinct.*

Suppose that the real symmetric matrix A has the minimum function

$$m(x) = (x_1 - x)^k \cdot h(x) \qquad k > 1.$$

Define $m_1(x)$ as follows:

$$m_1(x) = (x_1 - x)^{k-1} \cdot h(x).$$

Then $m(x)$ is a divisor of $[m_1(x)]^2$ so that

$$[m_1(A)]^2 = 0.$$

The matrix

$$m_1(A) = A_1 = (a_{rs})$$

is symmetric, since it is a polynomial in a symmetric matrix. Also $A_1^2 = 0$. Hence

$$\sum_{i=1}^{n} a_{ri} a_{is} = \sum_{i=1}^{n} a_{ri} a_{si} = 0$$

and in particular

$$\sum_{i=1}^{n} a_{ri}^2 = 0 \qquad r = 1, 2, \cdots, n.$$

Since the field is real, every element $a_{ri} = 0$ so that $A_1 = 0$. That is, $m_1(A) = 0$. But $m_1(x)$ is of lower degree than the minimum function $m(x)$, so that the hypothesis $k > 1$ is untenable, and x_1 is a simple root of $m(x) = 0$.

COROLLARY 83. *All the elementary divisors of a real symmetric matrix are linear.*

This is immediate, since every elementary divisor divides $m(x)$.

60. The orthogonal canonical form.

THEOREM 84. *Let A be a real symmetric matrix. There exists an orthogonal matrix P such that*

$$P^T A P = \begin{bmatrix} x_1 & & & & & & \\ & \ddots & & & & & \\ & & x_1 & & & & \\ & & & x_2 & & & \\ & & & & \ddots & & \\ & & & & & x_2 & \\ & & & & & & \ddots \\ & & & & & & & x_k \\ & & & & & & & & \ddots \\ & & & & & & & & & x_k \end{bmatrix}$$

where the x's are the characteristic roots of A.

By Theorem 83 and Corollary 82, the minimum function of A has the form

$$m(x) = (x_1 - x)(x_2 - x) \cdots (x_k - x)$$

where $x_1, x_2, \cdots, x_k$ are real and distinct. Let S_i', the null space of $x_i I - A$, be of dimension r_i. By Corollary 81 we can determine r_i linearly independent mutually orthogonal normalized vectors

$$\sigma_{i1}, \sigma_{i2}, \cdots, \sigma_{ir_i}$$

which span S_i'.

Form the matrix

$$P = \left[\sigma_{11}, \cdots, \sigma_{1r_1}, \sigma_{21}, \cdots, \sigma_{2r_2}, \cdots, \sigma_{k1}, \cdots, \sigma_{kr_k} \right].$$

By Theorem 55 the column vectors of P span the total space S, so that P is non-singular. By Theorem 82 each vector of the space S_i' is orthogonal to every vector of S_j' for $j \neq i$. Consequently P is an orthogonal matrix.

Since every vector of S_i' is annihilated by $x_i I - A$, it follows that

$$A\sigma_{11} = \sigma_{11}x_1, \cdots, A\sigma_{1r_1} = \sigma_{1r_1}x_1, \cdots,$$
$$A\sigma_{k1} = \sigma_{k1}x_k, \cdots, A\sigma_{kr_k} = \sigma_{kr_k}x_k.$$

These equations can all be combined into the one matric equation

$$AP = PB, \qquad P^T AP = B$$

where

$$B = \begin{bmatrix} x_1 & & & & & & & & \\ & \cdots & & & & & & & \\ & & x_1 & & & & & & \\ & & & x_2 & & & & & \\ & & & & \cdots & & & & \\ & & & & & x_2 & & & \\ & & & & & & \cdots & & \\ & & & & & & & x_k & \\ & & & & & & & & \cdots \\ & & & & & & & & x_k \end{bmatrix}$$

where x_i is repeated r_i times.

Since A and B are similar, they have the same characteristic roots, which are obviously the diagonal elements of B.

It should be noted that if the characteristic roots of A are all distinct, and if their order is specified, the orthogonal matrix P is unique except that the signs of the elements of any column may be reversed. In other cases it is not unique. Later we shall see the geometric consequences of this fact.

61. Principal axis transformation. Let F be any field. The polynomial

$$f(x_1, x_2, \cdots, x_n) = \sum_{i,j=1}^{n} a_{ij} x_i x_j$$

with coefficients in F is known as a *quadratic form* of *matrix* $A = (a_{rs})$. It is obviously no restriction to assume that $a_{ij} = a_{ji}$, so that every quadratic form has a symmetric matrix.

Let us introduce new variables by means of the linear homogeneous transformation

$$x_i = \sum_{j=1}^{n} p_{ij} x_j' \qquad i = 1, 2, \cdots, n,$$

and call $P = (p_{rs})$ the *matrix of the transformation*. Clearly f is transformed into a new quadratic form

$$f = \sum_{i,j=1}^{n} b_{ij} x_i' x_j'.$$

That is,

$$f = \sum_{i,j,k,l} a_{ij} p_{ik} p_{jl} x_k' x_l'.$$

Upon comparing coefficients we see that

$$b_{rs} = \sum_{i,j} a_{ij} p_{ir} p_{js}$$

which in matric notation is

$$B = P^T A P.$$

THEOREM 85. *If* $f(x_1, x_2, \cdots, x_n)$ *is a real quadratic form, we can determine an orthogonal transformation on the x's which reduces f to the form*

$$k_1 x_1'^2 + k_2 x_2'^2 + \cdots + k_n x_n'^2$$

where $k_1, k_2, \cdots, k_n$ *are the characteristic roots of the (symmetric) matrix of f.*

This follows directly from Theorem 84.

Let us apply this theorem to a problem in analytic geometry. In ordinary euclidean 3-space the equation

$$2x^2 + 2y^2 - 4z^2 - 2yz - 2xz - 5xy - 2x - 2y + z = 0$$

represents a quadric surface. We wish to find an orthogonal transformation which will eliminate the terms in xy, xz and yz. Since the second degree terms transform into second degree terms, and the linear terms into linear terms, we may for the moment ignore the latter. The form

$$f(x, y, z) = 2x^2 + 2y^2 - 4z^2 - 2yz - 2xz - 5xy$$

has the symmetric matrix

$$A = \begin{bmatrix} 2 & -\frac{5}{2} & -1 \\ -\frac{5}{2} & 2 & -1 \\ -1 & -1 & -4 \end{bmatrix}$$

whose characteristic equation is

$$x^3 - \frac{81}{4}x = 0.$$

Thus the characteristic roots are

$$k_1 = \frac{9}{2}, \qquad k_2 = -\frac{9}{2}, \qquad k_3 = 0.$$

The null space S_1' of $\frac{9}{2}I - A$ is spanned by the normalized vector

$$\phi_1 = (1/\sqrt{2}, -1/\sqrt{2}, 0),$$

and similarly the null space S_2' of $-\frac{9}{2}I - A$ is spanned by

$$\phi_2 = (1/3\sqrt{2}, 1/3\sqrt{2}, 4/3\sqrt{2})$$

and the null space S_3' of $-A$ is spanned by

$$\phi_3 = (\tfrac{2}{3}, \tfrac{2}{3}, -\tfrac{1}{3}).$$

The matrix

$$P = \begin{bmatrix} \dfrac{1}{\sqrt{2}} & \dfrac{1}{3\sqrt{2}} & \dfrac{2}{3} \\[2ex] \dfrac{-1}{\sqrt{2}} & \dfrac{1}{3\sqrt{2}} & \dfrac{2}{3} \\[2ex] 0 & \dfrac{4}{3\sqrt{2}} & -\dfrac{1}{3} \end{bmatrix}$$

is orthogonal, and by means of the orthogonal transformation having P as matrix, f is reduced to the form

$$\tfrac{9}{2}x'^2 - \tfrac{9}{2}y'^2,$$

and the equation of the quadric is reduced to a form in which the cross-product terms are absent.

If two of the characteristic roots had proved to be equal, the orthogonal matrix would not have been uniquely determined. This would mean that the quadric was a surface of revolution. If all three roots are equal, it is a sphere.

CHAPTER IX

ENDOMORPHISMS

62. Groups with operators. In this concluding chapter we shall treat vectors and matrices from a more abstract point of view and attempt to give the reader an insight into what is at the moment the popular mode of approach to matric theory.

The simplest important mathematical system is the *group*. A group consists of elements and a well-defined binary operation with respect to which the system is closed. That is, every ordered pair α, β of equal or distinct elements of the system determine a unique element γ of the system. We shall choose to denote the symbol of the operation by $+$ and to write

$$\alpha + \beta = \gamma.$$

In order that the system shall be a group it is necessary that the group operation be associative:

$$(\alpha + \beta) + \gamma = \alpha + (\beta + \gamma).$$

Thirdly, there must exist an identity element 0 such that

$$\alpha + 0 = 0 + \alpha = \alpha$$

for every group element α. And lastly, corresponding to each element α there must be an inverse $^-\alpha$ such that

$$^-\alpha + \alpha = \alpha + {}^-\alpha = 0.$$

If the group has the further property that for every pair of elements α and β

$$\alpha + \beta = \beta + \alpha,$$

then the group is said to be *commutative* or *abelian*.

In every commutative group G one may set up correspondences such as

$$(42) \qquad \alpha \rightarrow \alpha', \ \beta \rightarrow \beta', \ \cdots$$

by which every element of G determines a unique element of G. These primed elements may or may not constitute the whole of G. Such a correspondence will be called an *endomorphism* of G if for every two elements α and β of G it is true that

$$\alpha + \beta \rightarrow \alpha' + \beta'.$$

We may think of every endomorphism as being accomplished by an operator. We define k to be the operator such that

$$k\alpha = \alpha', \ k\beta = \beta', \ \cdots .$$

Since the correspondence is an endomorphism, k is a distributive operator:

$$k(\alpha + \beta) = \alpha' + \beta' = k\alpha + k\beta.$$

Every commutative group has at least two operators, the *zero operator* 0 such that*

$$0\alpha = 0$$

for every element α of G, and the *unit operator* 1 such that

$$1\alpha = \alpha$$

for every element α of G. For every operator k, $k0 = 0$, for

$$k\alpha = k(\alpha + 0) = k\alpha + k0.$$

---

* The context will indicate whether 0 is a group element or an operator and will make unnecessary the use of more elaborate notation.

Let k and l be two equal or distinct operators, and consider the correspondence

$$\alpha \rightarrow k\alpha + l\alpha.$$

This correspondence is an endomorphism, for

$$\alpha + \beta \rightarrow k(\alpha + \beta) + l(\alpha + \beta) = (k\alpha + k\beta) + (l\alpha + l\beta)$$
$$= (k\alpha + l\alpha) + (k\beta + l\beta).$$

This endomorphism we shall call the *sum* of the endomorphisms k and l, and denote by the symbol $k+l$. That is,

$$(k + l)\alpha = k\alpha + l\alpha.$$

If 0 is the zero operator,

$$(k + 0)\alpha = k\alpha + 0\alpha = k\alpha$$

for every element α of G. Since $k+0$ and k have the same effect upon every α, these operations are equal. Thus 0 is an identity element in the addition of operators (or endomorphisms).

Since $l\alpha, l\beta, \cdots$ are elements of G, so are

$$k(l\alpha), \; k(l\beta), \cdots$$

for all operators k and l. The correspondence

$$\alpha \rightarrow k(l\alpha), \; \beta \rightarrow k(l\beta), \cdots$$

is an endomorphism, for

$$\alpha + \beta \rightarrow k(l(\alpha + \beta)) = k(l\alpha + l\beta) = k(l\alpha) + k(l\beta).$$

This endomorphism we shall denote by the symbol kl, and call the *product* of the endomorphisms k and l. That is,

$$(kl)\alpha = k(l\alpha).$$

If 1 is the unit operator,

$$(k1)\alpha = k(1\alpha) = k\alpha, \qquad (1k)\alpha = 1(k\alpha) = k\alpha$$

for every group element α. Since $k1$ and $1k$ produce the same effect as k on every element α, it is true that

$$k1 = 1k = k.$$

Thus 1 is the unit element in the multiplication of endomorphisms.

Let us now consider the set Ω of all endomorphisms of a commutative group G. These endomorphisms, or operators, constitute the *operator domain* of G. We shall prove

THEOREM 86. *The operator domain Ω of a commutative group is a ring with unit element.*

To be a ring with unit element, the domain Ω must have the following properties:

1. The domain is a commutative group with respect to addition.

2. The domain is closed with respect to multiplication. Multiplication is associative, and there is a unit element.

3. Multiplication is distributive with respect to addition.

To establish the first property, we note that the sum of two operators is an operator, and that addition of operators is associative, since

$$\begin{aligned}
[k + (l + m)]\alpha &= k\alpha + (l + m)\alpha = k\alpha + (l\alpha + m\alpha) \\
&= (k\alpha + l\alpha) + m\alpha = (k + l)\alpha + m\alpha \\
&= [(k + l) + m]\alpha
\end{aligned}$$

for every element α of G. The unit of addition, as we have seen, is 0. For every element α of G,

$$ka + k(^-\alpha) = k(\alpha + {}^-\alpha) = k0 = 0$$

so that $k(^-\alpha)$ is an inverse $^-k\alpha$ of $k\alpha$. Finally, addition of operators is commutative if G is commutative.

We have seen that Ω is closed with respect to multiplication, and that 1 is the unit operator. Multiplication is associative, since

$$[k(lm)]\alpha = k[(lm)\alpha] = k[l(m\alpha)] = (kl)(m\alpha) = [(kl)m]\alpha$$

for every element α of G.

To prove the first distributive law, we note that

$$\begin{aligned}
[k(l+m)]\alpha &= k[(l+m)\alpha] = k[l\alpha + m\alpha] \\
&= k(l\alpha) + k(m\alpha) = (kl)\alpha + (km)\alpha \\
&= [kl + km]\alpha
\end{aligned}$$

for every element α of G. That is,

$$k(l+m) = kl + km.$$

Similarly we may show that

$$(k+l)m = km + lm.$$

63. Vector fields. A ring with unit element falls short of being a *field* unless multiplication is commutative and every element except the identity 0 of addition has an inverse with respect to multiplication.

As we have seen, the total operator domain Ω of a commutative group G is a ring with unit element. If Ω contains a proper subring Ω_1 with unit element, then Ω_1 is an operator domain of G properly contained in the total operator domain.

A commutative group with an operator domain Ω_1 (whether the total operator domain or not) which is a field is called a *vector space*.

If Ω_1 is a field, every operator $k \neq 0$ has an inverse k^{-1} such that $k^{-1}k = kk^{-1}$ is the unit operator 1. If, then, $k\alpha = 0$ with $k \neq 0$,

$$\alpha = 1\alpha = (k^{-1}k)\alpha = k^{-1}(k\alpha) = k^{-1}0 = 0.$$

The contrapositive of this statement is that, if $k\alpha = 0$ and $\alpha \neq 0$, then $k = 0$.

The significance of the assumption that F is a field may now be seen upon referring back to (42) where it was noted that the primed elements might not constitute the whole of G.

THEOREM 87. *If k is any operator of Ω_1 not the 0-operator, then*

$$k\alpha, \ k\beta, \ k\gamma, \ \cdots$$

are all distinct and constitute the whole of G. That is, k merely brings about a permutation of the elements of G.

Let G be the group of elements $\alpha, \beta, \gamma, \cdots$, and let G' be that subset of G which is composed of the elements $k\alpha, k\beta, k\gamma, \cdots$. Since $k \neq 0$, there is an operator k^{-1} of Ω_1 such that $kk^{-1} = 1$. Let η be any element of G. Then $k^{-1}\eta$ is an element of G such that

$$k(k^{-1}\eta) = (kk^{-1})\eta = 1\eta = \eta,$$

so that η is in G'.

If $k \neq 0$, the elements $k\alpha, k\beta, k\gamma, \cdots$ are all distinct, for $k\alpha = k\beta$ would imply

$$k\alpha - k\beta = k(\alpha - \beta) = 0$$

and consequently $\alpha - \beta = 0$.

We shall call a vector space S_n a *finite vector space* of *dimension n* if it contains n linearly independent elements while every set of $n+1$ elements are linearly dependent.

Let S_n be a finite vector space of dimension n, and let

$$\epsilon_1, \epsilon_2, \cdots, \epsilon_n$$

be n linearly independent elements of S_n. If α is any element of S_n, there exist $n+1$ numbers $b_1, b_2, \cdots, b_{n+1}$ of F not all 0 such that

$$b_1\epsilon_1 + b_2\epsilon_2 + \cdots + b_n\epsilon_n + b_{n+1}\alpha = 0.$$

If b_{n+1} were 0, at least one of the other b's would be different from 0, and this would imply a linear dependence relation among the ϵ's, which is not possible. Thus $b_{n+1} \neq 0$ and we may write

$$\alpha = a_1\epsilon_1 + a_2\epsilon_2 + \cdots + a_n\epsilon_n, \quad a_i = -b_i/b_{n+1},$$

or

$$\alpha = (a_1, a_2, \cdots, a_n) \begin{bmatrix} \epsilon_1 \\ \epsilon_2 \\ \cdots \\ \epsilon_n \end{bmatrix}.$$

This representation of α is unique, for if α had two such representations in terms of the ϵ's, their difference would yield a linear relation among the ϵ's.

Consider the correspondence

$$\alpha \leftrightarrow (a_1, a_2, \cdots, a_n)$$

where $(a_1, a_2, \cdots, a_n)$ is an n-tuple of numbers of the field F. This correspondence is biunique. Let addition and scalar multiplication of n-tuples be defined as in §7. Then, if

$$\beta = b_1\epsilon_1 + b_2\epsilon_2 + \cdots + b_n\epsilon_n, \quad \beta \leftrightarrow (b_1, b_2, \cdots, b_n)$$

is another element of the vector space,

$$\alpha + \beta \leftrightarrow (a_1 + b_1, a_2 + b_2, \cdots, a_n + b_n)$$

$$= (a_1, a_2, \cdots, a_n) + (b_1, b_2, \cdots, b_n)$$

and

$$k\alpha \leftrightarrow (ka_1, ka_2, \cdots, ka_n) = k(a_1, a_2, \cdots, a_n).$$

Consequently the correspondence is an isomorphism, and we have

THEOREM 88. *Every finite vector space of dimension n is isomorphic with a vector space of n-tuples of numbers of F as defined in §7.*

The representation of the vector space in terms of n-tuples of numbers of F is dependent upon the n linearly independent elements $\epsilon_1, \epsilon_2, \cdots, \epsilon_n$ which were chosen for the basis. It is clear from the theory of linear dependence that every basis is composed of the same number n of elements so that the concept of dimension is well defined.

Two isomorphic mathematical systems are abstractly identical as far as their properties with respect to the operations under consideration are concerned.

It is worthy of mention that for $n = 1$ this vector space becomes the field F.

There are vector spaces other than those composed of n-tuples of numbers of a field. For instance, consider the set of all polynomials in x with coefficients in an infinite field F. We may think of each polynomial as an n-tuple, where n is infinite, composed of all values which it assumes when x is replaced by the elements of F, or we may think of the polynomial as a vector merely because the postulates for a vector space are satisfied.

64. Matrices. Consider the total operator domain Ω of the commutative group G, and let F be a subdomain of Ω which is a field contained in the central of Ω. If $\mathfrak{a}$ is any operator of Ω defining the endomorphism

$$\alpha \rightarrow \alpha', \quad \beta \rightarrow \beta', \cdots$$

and if k is any operator of F, then because F is in the central of Ω,

$$\mathfrak{a}(k\alpha) = k(\mathfrak{a}\alpha) = k\alpha'$$

so that

$$k\alpha \rightarrow k\alpha'.$$

We may properly call $\mathfrak{a}$ an *endomorphism of the vector space S* defined by G and F.

We shall confine our attention to a finite vector space S_n of dimension n composed of all n-tuples of numbers of F. This vector space has a basis composed of n linearly independent vectors

$$\epsilon_1, \ \epsilon_2, \cdots, \ \epsilon_n.$$

Evidently the effect of an endomorphism on every element of S_n is known when its effect on the basic vectors is known. Let $\mathfrak{a}$ be an endomorphism of S_n under which

$$\epsilon_1 \rightarrow \epsilon_1', \ \epsilon_2 \rightarrow \epsilon_2', \cdots, \ \epsilon_n \rightarrow \epsilon_n'.$$

Since each vector ϵ_i' is uniquely expressible in the form

$$\epsilon_i' = a_{i1}\epsilon_1 + a_{i2}\epsilon_2 + \cdots + a_{in}\epsilon_n$$

where the a's are in F, we may write

$$\begin{bmatrix} \epsilon_1' \\ \epsilon_2' \\ \cdots \\ \epsilon_n' \end{bmatrix} = \begin{bmatrix} a_{11} & a_{12} \cdots a_{1n} \\ a_{21} & a_{22} \cdots a_{2n} \\ \cdot \ \cdot \ \cdot \ \cdot \ \cdot \ \cdot \ \cdot \\ a_{n1} & a_{n2} \cdots a_{nn} \end{bmatrix} \begin{bmatrix} \epsilon_1 \\ \epsilon_2 \\ \cdots \\ \epsilon_n \end{bmatrix}.$$

In matric notation this is

$$E' = AE \qquad\qquad A = (a_{rs}).$$

Hence

$$\mathfrak{a}E = \begin{bmatrix} \mathfrak{a}\epsilon_1 \\ \mathfrak{a}\epsilon_2 \\ \cdots \\ \mathfrak{a}\epsilon_n \end{bmatrix} = E' = AE.$$

Thus every endomorphism $\mathfrak{a}$ determines a unique matrix A with elements in F. This correspondence is actually biunique, for the ϵ_i' are uniquely determined by the matrix A. We shall write

$$\mathfrak{a} \leftrightarrow A.$$

In the endomorphism ring of S_n we have defined two operations, addition and multiplication. In the matric ring of order n over F we also have two operations denoted by addition and multiplication. A biunique correspondence

$$\mathfrak{a} \leftrightarrow A, \ \mathfrak{b} \leftrightarrow B, \ \cdots$$

is an isomorphism with respect to addition if

$$\mathfrak{a} + \mathfrak{b} \leftrightarrow A + B,$$

and is an isomorphism with respect to multiplication if*

$$\mathfrak{a}\mathfrak{b} \leftrightarrow BA.$$

The endomorphism ring will be isomorphic with the matric ring if it is isomorphic with it with respect to both addition and multiplication.

* The order in which the product is written is a purely notational matter.

THEOREM 89. *The endomorphism ring of the vector space S_n of dimension n over the field F is isomorphic with the ring of all matrices of order n over F.*

Let $\mathfrak{a}$ and $\mathfrak{b}$ be two endomorphisms, and let

$$\mathfrak{a} \leftrightarrow A, \qquad \mathfrak{b} \leftrightarrow B.$$

Then $\mathfrak{a}+\mathfrak{b}$ is the endomorphism which carries each vector ϵ_i into the vector $\mathfrak{a}\epsilon_i+\mathfrak{b}\epsilon_i$. But

$$(\mathfrak{a} + \mathfrak{b})E = \mathfrak{a}E + \mathfrak{b}E = AE + BE = (A + B)E$$

so that

$$\mathfrak{a} + \mathfrak{b} \leftrightarrow A + B.$$

Consider the matrix whose row vectors are the vectors

$$\phi_i = v_{i1}\epsilon_1 + v_{i2}\epsilon_2 + \cdots + v_{in}\epsilon_n.$$

Clearly

$$\begin{bmatrix} \phi_1 \\ \phi_2 \\ \cdots \\ \phi_n \end{bmatrix} = \begin{bmatrix} v_{11} & v_{12} \cdots v_{1n} \\ v_{21} & v_{22} \cdots v_{2n} \\ \cdots \cdots \cdots \\ v_{n1} & v_{n2} \cdots v_{nn} \end{bmatrix} \begin{bmatrix} \epsilon_1 \\ \epsilon_2 \\ \cdots \\ \epsilon_n \end{bmatrix} = VE.$$

From the definition of endomorphism we have

$$\mathfrak{a}\phi_i = v_{i1}\mathfrak{a}\epsilon_1 + v_{i2}\mathfrak{a}\epsilon_2 + \cdots + v_{in}\mathfrak{a}\epsilon_n$$

so that

$$\mathfrak{a}VE = \begin{bmatrix} \mathfrak{a}\phi_1 \\ \mathfrak{a}\phi_2 \\ \cdots \\ \mathfrak{a}\phi_n \end{bmatrix} = \begin{bmatrix} v_{11} & v_{12} \cdots v_{1n} \\ v_{21} & v_{22} \cdots v_{2n} \\ \cdots \cdots \cdots \\ v_{n1} & v_{n2} \cdots v_{nn} \end{bmatrix} \begin{bmatrix} \mathfrak{a}\epsilon_1 \\ \mathfrak{a}\epsilon_2 \\ \cdots \\ \mathfrak{a}\epsilon_n \end{bmatrix} = V(\mathfrak{a}E).$$

Now we may complete the proof of Theorem 89. Evidently

$$(\mathfrak{a}\mathfrak{b})E = \mathfrak{a}(\mathfrak{b}E) = \mathfrak{a}BE = B(\mathfrak{a}E) = B(AE) = (BA)E.$$

Hence

$$\mathfrak{a}\mathfrak{b} \leftrightarrow BA.$$

65. Change of basis. An endomorphism of a vector space, as we have defined it, is an absolute concept and does not involve the concept of basis. The matric representation of the endomorphism, however, appears to depend upon the basis chosen. When we pass from one basis to another we should therefore expect the total matric ring to undergo an *automorphism*—that is, an isomorphism with itself. We shall now see how this takes place.

If $\epsilon_1, \epsilon_2, \cdots, \epsilon_n$ and $\eta_1, \eta_2, \cdots, \eta_n$ are two bases of S_n, they are related in the manner

$$\eta_i = \sum t_{ij}\epsilon_j \qquad\qquad T = (t_{rs})$$

where the elements t_{ij} are in F and T is a non-singular matrix. These equations may be written

$$H = TE, \qquad H = \begin{bmatrix} \eta_1 \\ \eta_2 \\ \cdots \\ \eta_n \end{bmatrix}.$$

If $\mathfrak{a}$ is an endomorphism, let

$$\mathfrak{a}E = AE, \qquad \mathfrak{a}H = A'H$$

so that, relative to the ϵ-basis $\mathfrak{a} \leftrightarrow A$ and relative to the η-basis $\mathfrak{a} \leftrightarrow A'$. Then

$$\mathfrak{a}H = \mathfrak{a}TE = T\mathfrak{a}E = TAE.$$

Also

$$\mathfrak{a}H = A'H = A'TE.$$

Since the ϵ's are linearly independent, $A'T = TA$, or

$$A' = TAT^{-1}.$$

We have proved

THEOREM 90. *Under a change of basis of matrix T, the matrix $A \leftrightarrow \mathfrak{a}$ is transformed into the similar matrix TAT^{-1}.*

The correspondence

$$A \leftrightarrow TAT^{-1}, \ B \leftrightarrow TBT^{-1}, \cdots$$

is clearly an automorphism of the total matric ring. For it is biunique, and

$$TAT^{-1} + TBT^{-1} = T(A \mid B)T^{-1},$$
$$TAT^{-1} \cdot TBT^{-1} = T(AB)T^{-1}$$

so that

$$A + B \leftrightarrow T(A + B)T^{-1}, \qquad AB \leftrightarrow T(AB)T^{-1}.$$

An automorphism obtained by multiplying all the matrices of the ring on the left by the same non-singular matrix T and on the right by T^{-1} is called an *inner automorphism* of the ring.

If $\epsilon_1, \epsilon_2, \cdots, \epsilon_n$ is any basis for S_n, and if T is any non-singular matrix with elements in F, the vectors

$$\eta_i = \sum t_{ij}\epsilon_j \qquad\qquad T = (t_{rs})$$

constitute a basis for S_n. Thus if $\mathfrak{a}$ is an automorphism of matrix A, and if A' is any matrix similar to A, a basis for S_n may be chosen with respect to which $\mathfrak{a} \leftrightarrow A'$. Now from Theorem 68 we have

THEOREM 91. *A basis for the vector space S_n may be so chosen that any particular endomorphism has a matrix which is a direct sum of matrices of Type* (35).

The abstract approach to matric theory by way of vector spaces has certain advantages of elegance over the classical approach. Thus there is no question as to how the sum, product and scalar product of matrices must be defined if the correspondence between endomorphisms and matrices is to be an isomorphism. Once this isomorphism is established, the associative and distributive laws, etc., which are so obvious for endomorphisms, are necessarily effective for matrices. The necessity and reasonableness of these rules of combination are more directly apparent.

BIBLIOGRAPHY

1. Lattès, S. *Sur une forme canonique nouvelle des substitutions linèaires.* Ann. Fac. Sci. Univ. Toulouse, vol. 28 (1914), 1–84.

2. Kowalewski, G. *Natürliche Normalformen linearer Transformationen.* Ber. Verh. sächs. Akad., Leipzig, vol. 68 (1916), 325–335.

3. Krull, W. *Ueber Begleitmatrizen und Elementarteilertheorie.* Freiburg, 1921.

4. Weyl, H. *Mathematische Analyse des Raumproblems.* Springer, Berlin, 1923.

5. Dickson, L. E. *Modern algebraic theories.* Sanborn, Chicago, 1926. Chap. V.

6. Krull, W. *Theorie und Anwendung der verallgemeinerten Abelschen Gruppen.* S.-B. Heidelberg Akad. Wiss., 1926. 32 pp.

7. Bennett, A. A. *Construction of a rational canonical form for a linear transformation.* Amer. Math. Monthly, vol. 38 (1931), 377–383.

8. van der Waerden, B. L. *Moderne Algebra,* vol. II, Springer, Berlin, 1931. Chap. XV.

9. Turnbull, H. W. and A. C. Aitken. *An introduction to the theory of canonical matrices.* Blackie, London, 1932. Chap. V.

10. Schreier, O. and E. Sperner. *Vorlesungen über Matrizen.* Teubner, Leipzig, 1932.

11. Ingraham, M. H. *On the reduction of a matrix to its rational canonical form.* Bull. Amer. Math. Soc., vol. 39 (1933), 379–382.

12. Menge, W. O. *Construction of transformations to canonical forms.* Amer. J. Math., vol. 55 (1933), 671–682.

13. MacDuffee, C. C. *The theory of matrices.* Ergebnisse der Mathematik und ihrer Grenzgebiete, vol. 2 (1933). Chap. VI.

14. Wedderburn, J. H. M. *Lectures on matrices.* American Mathematical Society Colloquium Publications, vol. 17, New York, 1934.

15. Gantmacher, F. *The geometric theory of elementary divisors according to Krull.* (Russian.) Trans. Univ. Odessa, Math. 1, 1935, 89–108.

16. Albert, A. A. *Modern higher algebra.* Univ. of Chicago Press, 1937. Chap. IV.

17. Ingraham, M. H. and M. C. Wolf. *Relative linear sets and similarity of matrices whose elements belong to a division algebra.* Trans. Amer. Math. Soc., vol. 42 (1937), 16–31.

18. Cavallucci, L. *Riduzione di una matrice alla forma canonica nel suo campo di razionalità*. Rend. Semin. mat. Univ. Padova, vol. 16 (1937), 92–109.

19. Cramlet, C. M. *On the reduction of a representation to classical canonical form*. Amer. Math. Monthly, vol. 45 (1938), 159–162.

20. Wedderburn, J. H. M. *The canonical form of a matrix*. Ann. of Math. IIs., vol. 39 (1938), 178–180.

21. Jacobson, N. *Notes on modern higher algebra*. Univ. of North Carolina, 1940.

22. Browne, E. T. *On the reduction of a matrix to canonical form*. Amer. Math. Monthly, vol. 47 (1940), 437–450.

23. Varineau, V. J. *An extension of the theory of matrices with elements in a principal ideal ring*. Univ. of Wisconsin Libraries, 1940.

24. Albert, A. A. *Introduction to algebraic theories*. Univ. of Chicago Press, 1941. Chap. IV.

25. Petr, K. *Rationale kanonische Form einer linearen Substitution*. Cas. math. fys., vol. 69 (1940), 9–22.

26. Smiley, M. F. *The rational canonical form of a matrix*. Amer. Math. Monthly, vol. 49 (1942), 451–454.

INDEX OF TERMS